Underwater Observation Using Sonar

Underwater Observation Using Sonar

by D. G. Tucker
Professor and Head of Department of
Electronic and Electrical Engineering,
University of Birmingham

Fishing News (Books) Limited
110 Fleet Street, London, E.C.4

Other books by the author
relevant to this subject

Applied Underwater Acoustics—D. G. Tucker and B. K. Gazey
(Published by Pergamon Press 1966)

On other subjects

Modulators and Frequency Changers
(Published by Macdonald 1953)

Elementary Electrical Network Theory
(Published by Pergamon 1964)

Circuits with Periodically Varying Parameters
(Published by Macdonald 1964)

Printed by The Whitefriars Press Limited, London and Tonbridge

Contents

List of Illustrations

Preface

In preparing the Buckland Lectures for 1966 on "Sonar in Fisheries" it quickly became apparent to me that there was a need for a simple book explaining the problems of underwater observation in general, why sonar is so important in this field and how it works. While simple, the treatment would never-theless have to be sufficiently thorough and quantitative to enable a keen user not only to understand in a general sense how his sonar works, but to be able to calculate approximately its expected performance and the effect of changes in the design. The present book is my attempt to provide this treat-ment. Its mathematical demands are very small and its demands on a knowledge of physics hardly exceed those of "O" level in the General Certificate of Education. In addition to providing information for those actually concerned with sonar, I hope it will also be suitable for general reading by inquiring laymen and students.

As a research engineer, I have not felt qualified to discuss the operational use of sonar by fishermen and, indeed, there are already some good small books on this subject.* Nor have I thought it desirable to give descriptions or illustrations of the actual hardware of commercial sonar equipments, as these are readily available in the various sales brochures of the manu-facturers. While I have felt it essential to give a general review of the whole field of underwater observation in Chapter 1, partly, of course, because of its interest but mainly to show where sonar fits into the scheme of things, it must nevertheless be understood that in this matter I can claim no professional

* See, for example, "The Uses of Echo Sounding for Fishermen" by D. H. Cushing, H.M. Stationery Office, 1963; also several books published by the manufacturers of sonar equipment.

competence. It is only on sonar that I write as a professional. But I have had my manuscript read by experts and, although I had better not name them, I am grateful for their corrections and advice.

I would like to thank Mr. Ronald Balls and Sir Alister Hardy (and their publishers) for permission to quote extracts from their books, and the owners of the various photographic illustrations (individually acknowledged in the captions) for the supply of original photographs and for permission to use them.

D. G. T.

Extract from

"Fish Capture"

by Skipper Ronnie Balls

(being the Buckland Lectures for 1959)
Skipper Balls was one of the pioneers of echo-fishing

All fishing is groping in the dark; and the echo-sounder has brought an extra sensitivity which is more than giving the blind man a stick. It is like giving him the radar sensitivity of the bat: not sight, but the next thing to it.

We are still too close to see this change in true perspective. We can look back at the milestones: the baited trap, the boat, the moving net, the coming of steam power; all these mark the great steps in man's fishing progress. Now the echo-sounder, and this is by far the greatest advance in a thousand years of fishing: what it will lead to no one knows.

The practice of fishing by echo has become general since about 1950, when plenty of recording-type sounders came on the market. It is most effective with the shoaling fishes.

In all the great herring, menhaden, pilchard and similar fisheries of Norway, Alaska, the Pacific coast, Scotland and South Africa, as well as Russia and Japan, skippers now study the echo-sounder to locate the shoals before they use their purse seines, lamparas, trawls or gill nets to capture them. This is the space-age fishing: fishing by sight almost. It is safe to say that production has been increased many times by the use of these electronic fish-finders and the methods built around them.

Chapter 1
Getting information
under water

1   Introduction

Interest in the seas and oceans and in what goes on under water
has grown rapidly in recent years, and in many countries a very
large amount of money is spent in oceanographical and fisheries
work of a vast variety. Some of this interest arises from the
difficulties which traditional fisheries are meeting nowadays
and the need to obtain more food from the sea while fish stocks
seem to be in some danger of serious depletion; some arises from
the needs of communications, e.g. ships and cables, and from
civil engineering; some from the search for new supplies of oil;
some from military and naval needs, the operation of long-
range submarines and weapons, and so on; and some of the
interest arises from human curiosity—the need to understand
our environment which is inborn in intelligent humans.
Doubtless different interests have different relative weights in
different countries and we cannot pursue this very far here.

Britain, as a maritime nation with a long tradition of commercial, naval and fishing activity, has a very long-standing
interest in the study of the oceans, and was indeed a pioneer in
the systematic and scientific approach to it. Recently, however,
there has been an enormous expansion in ocean activity in the
United States, Japan and Russia, and British efforts have not
expanded in the same way.* It is to be hoped that this will
soon be rectified. But the British work in oceanography and
fisheries has been important enough and its now relatively
small scale forces a greater concentration on matters of real
significance. The Fisheries Laboratories at Lowestoft and the
Marine Laboratories at Aberdeen, the National Institute of
Oceanography, numerous smaller laboratories operated by

---

* It is worth noting that the British fishing industry is not a large one by world
standards; some countries catch perhaps ten times as much fish. Nevertheless, it is
still quite sizeable, the value of the catch as landed being about £60 million per
annum; this represents probably nearly £300 million per annum at the consumer.

universities, research associations, and by industrial and Government organizations, and more recently the White Fish Authority, have in various ways contributed to advances in marine science and technology.

An examination of the programmes and achievements of these various bodies concerned with advancing underwater activity will quickly show that a large proportion of their effort is devoted to developing means of gathering information about what goes on underwater. Not only does the progress of research itself depend on this, but so also nowadays does the everyday activity of marine operations. Fishermen expect more and more to be able to obtain information from their instruments about what there is in and under the sea, so do navigators, sub-mariners, divers and others. No longer is reliance on local knowledge and long experience considered adequate.

Although this book is primarily concerned with acoustic systems of gathering information in fisheries operations and research, we must continue the process of putting things into perspective by examining the various kinds of information which are needed underwater, the various ways in which this information can be obtained, and some of the engineering principles involved. We shall then be ready to concentrate on the application of acoustics.

2   The kinds of information needed in various fields of activity

The various fields will be considered in their order of importance to fishermen, but it will soon be seen that they almost all have relevance to fishing.

2.1   *Fish catching*

Presumably, if it were possible, a fishing skipper would like ideally a complete, immediately up-to-date, immediately available map of the whole fishing area—e.g. the North Sea— showing the exact location, extent, density, depth, movement, species and size of all fish shoals, together with details of the sea-bottom such as depth, contours, slopes, roughness, stones, rocks, etc. Of course, there is no prospect in the foreseeable future of being able to get anything like this in practice. Present techniques suggest no approach to such complete information on any practicable or economic basis. In principle it might be just conceivable that innumerable short-range, high-resolution acoustic or optical equipments could be located at such a density that all this information could be gathered and relayed to a vast central computer installation by means of cable or other communication links. But obviously such a system is completely beyond our resources. This is not to say that it must for ever be so; new developments in electronics such as micro-miniaturization, and in other branches of science and engineering, may one day make such a system practicable and economic—but this is in the more distant future. We must, therefore, look at the problem to see what kind of cruder information will suffice. After all, until this generation, no aids were available at all, and yet fish were caught economically. But it is no longer economic to fish completely without modern aids.

The main features of the sea-bottom relevant to fishing are known from long experience by many fishing skippers. The author remembers how some years ago a Lowestoft skipper was able to draw up a map of a large portion of the North Sea, marking in from memory the areas of sand, shingle, stones, ross, etc. The depths and contours are already marked in coarse detail on the Admiralty charts, and special fishing charts are also available. But for this information to be really useful, accurate navigation is necessary and a great deal of experience too—and even then it is only very crude information. Clearly some device which gives an immediate portrayal of the bottom conditions without need of accurate navigation would be advantageous.

By contrast with sea-bottom information, however, the need for information on the whereabouts and nature of fish shoals is of an entirely different order. Experience will tell the skipper which area or "fishing grounds" might be profitable to visit, but he cannot know beforehand whether worth-while concentrations of fish will be there. One can imagine that one type of crude information which would be useful would be the results of a regular and frequent survey of the area by special survey ships equipped with fish-detection gear of some kind. The information as to the distribution of fish shoals could then be broadcast by radio to all fishing boats, which could thus concentrate on the areas where fish were reported. Such information would never, of course, be up-to-date and by the time the fishing boats reached an area the fish might have gone. In any case, the survey cannot be made fast or thorough. Some service of this kind is indeed provided already on a limited basis in some areas.

For demersal fishing, where fish such as cod, haddock, whiting and flat fish lying on or within a few feet of the sea-bottom are caught by trawl* or other bottom-gathering net which makes a long haul of perhaps 10 miles over the bottom, there is inevitably a large element of chance involved in the size of catch, since the boat and its trawl can hardly weave about rapidly to catch odd shoals which may be detected to one side or other of its track. All that can be done is to trawl along a track which seems to include the greatest overall number of fish near the bottom. If all the fish within a 10-mile range could be quickly observed from the trawler by some means, then the best track could be determined accurately and catches could be maximized. But this is not at present possible, nor is it likely to be in the foreseeable future. So the catch remains a matter of chance. This is not to say, however, that there is no value in either the area survey system mentioned above, or in efficient methods of examining fish shoals at ranges much less than 10 miles. Both of these can, or could, reduce the element of chance considerably. The extent of the benefit produced is still hotly debated by fisheries experts.†

For pelagic fishing, where herring, sprat, pilchard, and mackerel are caught in the upper layers of the sea, a rather different situation is found. Here the catching techniques—mainly the drift net, ring net and purse seine net—do not depend primarily on scouring a large area like the bottom trawl does, but rather on intercepting or encircling the fish shoals. Knowledge of fish behaviour is helpful; for example, herring appear to rise from mid water to the surface at night and

---

* For a description of the modern trawl, Sir Alister Hardy's opening remarks in his book "The Open Sea, Part II: Fish and Fisheries" (Collins New Naturalist, London, 1959) can hardly be surpassed; they are reproduced as Appendix I in this book.

† See, for example, the paper by R. E. Craig, and the discussion by D. H. Cushing thereon: "The Fisheries Application of Sonar", J. Brit. Inst. Radio Engrs., 25, 1963, pp. 201–206.

consequently drifting for herring is usually done at night. But as the fish are more easily detected by echo-sounder when in midwater, they can be located before dark and be assumed to rise later. They must, however, be recognized as herring.

It is clear that for these interception methods of fishing, there is a premium on knowing the presence and location of fish and also if possible their species and size and numbers or density. The chance element which has to dominate in bottom trawling is desirably removed from pelagic fishing, and this means that efficient methods of observing fish at a reasonable distance are required. It is, of course, better than nothing if the fish can be observed beneath the ship as with an echo-sounder, but clearly it is much more advantageous to observe them at some distance from the ship's position so that the net can be more readily manoeuvred around them (in the case of the ring or purse seine nets) or put in a position to entangle them (as with the drift net).

Some pelagic fishing is done with midwater trawls. This appears to be of growing importance. It is necessary in this case to know not only where the fish are (and what they are) but also to be able to set the trawl at the right depth. This means that a method of observing the mouth of the net is required, or at any rate a method of determining its depth.

Other kinds of fishing, such as long-line fishing, are important in other parts of the world; but the methods discussed above are those most important in British fisheries.

To sum up the kinds of information needed in fish catching, we see that the skipper needs general information on the distribution of fish shoals over a large area, but once having found a suitable fishing ground needs to get the fish into the net, which is not directly under the boat. There is, therefore, a need for observing shoals at some distance (say half-a-mile) from the boat. Information on species of fish, size of fish and their density in the shoal, together with their distribution between sea-surface and bottom is ideally needed. Skilled fishermen can guess a lot of this from very limited instrumental observations because they know the habits of the fish. The commercial value of better methods is not easy to assess, but must be real. Information on the nature of the sea-bottom is important in bottom trawling, and is desirably directly observed from the ship; but again, experienced skippers have a good accumulated knowledge of their regular areas, although accurate navigation is needed to make use of it.

2.2 Fisheries research

Fisheries research is a very wide and varied subject, covering topics from the breeding biology of fish and plankton to the behaviour of, and stresses and strains in, the gear used for fish catching. It includes the study of population dynamics, migration, responses of fish to external stimuli, etc. In all aspects of this work some means of observation and gathering information is always required, but we shall limit our consideration here to two particular branches of fisheries research where the underwater information involved is of the kind which sonar systems are best able to provide. These are the behaviour of fish in relation to the catching process and the behaviour of underwater gear.

Fishermen drag trawls over the sea-bottom and the weighted footrope and its bobbins (i.e. rollers) disturb fish lying on the bottom. The headrope is well ahead of the footrope, so that there is a roof of net above these fish. But how many escape round the sides? Are fish sufficiently sensitive to sound to be disturbed by the noise of the footrope on the bottom far enough ahead even to escape upwards before the headrope arrives? Is the shape of the trawl opening accurately known? It is known that fish can be herded by large-mesh nets without escaping through the meshes, but how do different species compare in this respect? The answers to such questions are generally vague. It is known that fish are responsive to sound, their hearing mechanism has been investigated, and experiments have been carried out in large tanks to see how their movements are affected by low-frequency sound waves, by moving nets, and so on. But the questions still cannot be answered properly. A direct means of observing the fish and the net in an operational situation is required. (See Fig. 1.)

Although midwater and surface-water nets such as the pelagic trawl and the purse seine net do not have noisy footropes banging on the sea-bottom, the drag of the ropes and net through the water nevertheless causes an acoustic wave to be transmitted which undoubtedly affects fish behaviour in relation to the nets, but again observation in the sea is necessary for the effect to be studied and assessed. Is the shape and behaviour of a seine net really as shown in the usual diagrams and is it always a stable shape or can it "flap"? Means of obtaining accurate dimensional information on such nets are clearly required.

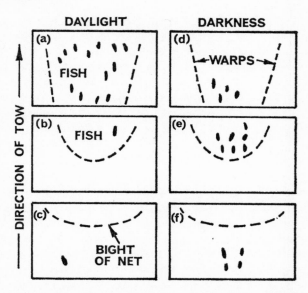

Fig. 1.—Sketches made from the display tube of an experimental high-resolution sonar equipment which gives a plan view of the objects in the water. The observations show the effect of the net being towed through the water on the herding of the fish. The pattern of herding was found to alter as the light intensity dropped. The three diagrams on the left (a, b, and c) show different stages in the haul in daylight, and the three on the right (d, e, and f) show corresponding stages in darkness. The herding effect is evidently greater in daylight; at night the fish get nearer the net and more pass through it.

(From an article by V. G. Welsby, J. H. S. Blaxter and C. J. Chapman in Nature, Vol. 199, 1963, p. 980.)

It is well known that fish of a particular species are sometimes plentiful and sometimes scarce in a given area. The causes of their migrations and fluctuations may be due to food supply and temperature variations and so on, but it has been suggested that it would be helpful to know how they find their way about and that direct observation of fish movements in relation to tidal currents, etc., would be useful to determine whether or not the direction of water flow over the sea-bottom appears to be used as a means of navigation. Some preliminary work shows that sonar could be used for this.

As a result of the availability of a crude means of direct observation of fish—i.e. the echo-sounder—it is now well known that many fish vary their shoaling behaviour and depth according to the amount of light at the surface. The deep scattering layer (d.s.l.)—an important layer of organisms that is found widely in the deeper seas—was discovered only as a result of the use of echo-sounders (see Fig. 2), and its further investigation is dependent on the development of more refined observation equipment. A large-scale investigation of the d.s.l. was organized by the National Institute of Oceanography in the Autumn of 1965 using a whole battery of echo-sounders of different frequencies to increase the information obtained. A fuller account of the d.s.l. is given in Appendix II.

2.3   *Oceanography*

Oceanography is the study of the seas and oceans in all its scientific aspects. Although not fundamentally concerned with exploiting the knowledge gained, oceanographers can hardly be unconcerned entirely, and thus pay a good deal of attention to matters which closely affect fisheries. In its biological side, oceanography includes the study of numerous marine organisms which are either caught by fishermen or form the food of the fish which are caught. In its physical side, oceanography includes the study of currents in shallow and deep water, the tides, circulation of chemical components of the sea-water which may be nutrients for plant and animal life, the variations of temperature and mixing of different kinds of water, etc. These matters affect fisheries in a quite direct way. Other physical studies which still affect fishing operations, but, perhaps less directly, include waves and their generation, methods of forecasting storms, waves and swell and thus of avoiding them, the heat flow from the ocean floor to the water, and so on.

The majority of these matters are incapable of direct visual observation and measurement, and methods of measuring and observing underwater over considerable distances are needed. In some cases instruments such as thermometers, current meters, salinity-measuring equipment, pressure recorders, etc., are placed remotely on the sea-floor or in the water and their information has to be relayed to a ship or to shore over some sort of telemetry link. Currents can be measured by means of a float which drifts with the current at a predetermined depth, and whose position at different times can be determined by taking bearings on a sound source contained in the float, from a number of shipborne underwater sound receivers. In other cases visual and acoustic systems are used to observe at a distance, e.g. underwater television and sonar.

2.4 *Navigation*

The need for accurate navigation has been acknowledged right down the centuries, but progress was slow, relying on visual observation of land or sky, with a leisurely development of simple instruments such as the sextant and chronometer to put navigation on a quantitative basis. The history of ocean exploration in the sixteenth (and even the seventeenth) century is still full of mistaken locations and until longitude could be measured properly (using an accurate chronometer as the basis) errors of location of hundreds of miles were usual. Yet nowadays, in many areas, it is possible for a ship to locate itself within a few yards, although out of sight of land, by using modern radio techniques. Many fishing boats are, of course, not fitted with equipment suitable for this, as it is expensive.

The need for underwater information in navigation is, naturally, rather less when full radio-navigation equipment is carried than when it is not. But few captains and skippers would feel adequately equipped without an echo-sounder to show the depth of water under the ship. It is possible to contemplate navigation almost entirely by echo-sounder in certain places and conditions (e.g. a traffic-free estuary in fog), and indeed an automatic contour-following navigational system has been suggested.

One wonders whether a means of observing objects underwater which are not approximately beneath the ship would not be very desirable in many circumstances. For example, not so long ago a large ship was lost on her maiden voyage, supposedly through collision with an iceberg. She was well equipped with radio aids, but as icebergs may extend further under the surface than above it, a horizontal-beam sonar might well have saved the ship. (See Fig. 3.)

2.5 *Marine geology*

Geologists and geophysicists need to know a great deal about the sea-floor in order to follow out the geological system observed more readily on land and to predict the existence of oil. The development of oil prospecting in the North Sea is evidence enough of this latter interest.

The sorts of information which are required for one purpose or another are the material forming the sea-floor, the depth of the different layers of sediment and rock, the nature of the surface of the sea-floor (smooth, stony, rocky, etc.) and the orientation and slopes of the rock strata. Much of this information is of interest to the fisherman as has previously been noted.

In addition to this purely geological data, other features of the sea-bed of concern to fishermen include the undulations and ridging of sand often known as sand-waves. Small-scale examples of this phenomenon are seen on most sandy shores between the tide-marks; these have wavelengths and heights measured in centimetres. In greater depths and tidal currents, e.g. in some parts of the North Sea, sand-waves have wavelengths and heights measured in metres or tens of metres. Methods of observing the sea-floor must be capable of recording these sand-waves.

2.6 *Civil engineering*

Under this heading we include matters pertaining to harbours, piers and breakwaters, etc., and to coastal protection, erosion and accretion of land, etc. These matters are of less direct interest to fishermen than those discussed above, but are none the less of importance to them.

Scour and silting in harbours need to be observed under-water and means of doing so really efficiently and quickly are not readily available.

2.7 *Diving*

Diving is, of course, itself a means of observing things under-water, and divers can be used to observe scour and silting in harbours mentioned above. They can search for objects on the harbour- or sea-floor, investigate wrecks, carry out minor underwater repairs to ships, and so on. But the diver's vision underwater may be very poor—in many situations the water is almost opaque—and some aid to observation is advantageous. Also, communication between the diver and his ship or the shore needs to be good; the old-fashioned rope signal is not adequate and a good telephonic communication system is needed. (See Fig. 4.)

2.8 *Naval and military operations*

This kind of subject is difficult to discuss freely, but is fortunately not very closely associated with the normal activities of the fishing industry. All sorts of underwater observations are required, e.g. the detection and tracking of submarines, torpedoes, etc., and the location of objects on the sea-floor. By and large the newer techniques used in fishing operations— e.g. sonar—have evolved first in the naval sphere. But the operational requirements of equipment for naval and fishing use are very different. For one thing, cost is very much more important in the fishing world, and reliability, though still of importance, is rather less critical. Yet fishing equipment has to be operated without having technical experts at hand. Electrical power is at a premium on fishing boats, but is plentiful on naval vessels. But fundamentally the underwater observational needs of naval and military operations are much the same as those of fishing operations.

3 The possible methods of getting underwater information

We shall now review the various methods which are available for getting the kinds of underwater information which we have discussed above. Although our main aim in this book is to discuss acoustic methods, it is clearly necessary to view these in relation to all the other possible methods and to be clear as to what are the circumstances in which acoustic methods are superior.

3.1 *Direct sampling*

Direct methods of obtaining information were, of course, the earliest used. The sounding lead, later on filled with tallow to

retain a sample of the bottom material, has a history dating
from the earliest records. Attempts to make accurate studies
of the oceans developed surprisingly late, however, and it was
not until the early part of the nineteenth century that serious
measurements of the depth of the ocean were commenced,
using a weighted line. The development of submarine cables
accelerated the taking of soundings, and by the time of the
Great War of 1914 about 6,000 deep ocean soundings had been
taken. The measurement of depth using a long wire line (as
refined by Lord Kelvin) is still not entirely obsolete. But it is
obviously a very clumsy and long-winded business, requiring a
great deal of skill to operate, and it is not surprising that the
simplicity and accuracy of the acoustic echo-sounder has
almost entirely displaced it, for both shallow- and deep-water
use.

The sounding lead had the advantage, already mentioned, of
bringing up a sample of the material of the sea-bottom. This
had value from both the research and the navigational point of
view—the latter because the material could help to identify
the mariner's location if he had previous knowledge of the area.
But obviously the sample was, scientifically speaking, not a good
one since only the smaller particles and stones would adhere to
the tallow. So more refined (and more complicated) methods of
direct sampling were developed to take "cores"; a tube of a
few inches diameter is driven, by heavy weights affixed to it,
into the sea-bottom for several (or even many) feet, and thus
brings up a sample showing the layers of bottom material in
their proper order (see Figs. 5 and 6). It is fair to say that no
better method of getting this information has yet been developed,
and for this particular study the direct-sampling process holds
its own. Grabs and dredges are also used for sampling the top
layer of the sea-bottom, especially when large stones and rocks
are involved. The extreme case of direct sampling is no doubt
the Mohole project for penetrating the earth's crust under the
sea and sampling the mantle itself.

For studying the sea-water and its temperature distribution,
direct sampling still plays an important part. Special "reversing
bottles" are used for this purpose. They are lowered on a wire
(a number of bottles is usually fitted, one for each depth at
which observations are required) and when operated by a

messenger weight dropped down the wire, their valves close and a sample of water is trapped, its temperature being recorded by a special kind of thermometer whose mercury thread is broken by the reversing action so that the amount cut off corresponds to the temperature of the sample *in situ* (see Fig. 7). The salinity and other chemical properties of the sample can be measured later on. For shallow-water work, insulated sampling bottles may be used instead with ordinary thermometers inside them.

For direct sampling of the living organisms of the sea, various grabs (for bottom-living organisms) and trawls and nets (for mid-water organisms such as plankton and fish) are used. Some of the latter are not unlike the trawls used by fishermen, although they are much smaller. (See Fig. 8.)

It seems likely that direct sampling will always have a place in marine studies, but it has many disadvantages. It does not always follow that the sample is typical, and it may well (as in the simple example of the tallow in the lead) be largely a function of the design of the sampler. When the sampling can be supplemented by other methods—e.g. the taking of an underwater photograph of the small area of sea-bottom from which a grab sample is obtained—it becomes far more useful. But the clumsiness of the direct sampling methods means that relatively few observations can be made. So there is continuous development of observing instruments which give an immediate and continuous record, and/or a more reliable observation.

3.2 *Direct observation*

The disadvantages of direct sampling in respect of such matters as the surface structure of the sea-floor and the larger animal life in the sea can to some extent be overcome by the use of direct observation, i.e. by human observers descending into the sea in diving suits or bathyscaphes to see for themselves. Although in diving suits man can descend only a few hundred feet, yet in special pressure-resisting structures the greatest depths can be reached, and the Piccards' bathyscaphe "Trieste" descended to 35,800 feet in the Marianas Trench (in the western Pacific) in 1960. Mobile manned underwater vehicles for research purposes are now being developed.

Direct observation has serious limitations of its own, however. apart from the enormous cost of the equipment for great depths,

These arise from three factors, closely connected: the lack of clarity in the sea, the attenuation (or weakening) of light-waves due to transmission in the sea, and the low level of natural illumination at the greater depths.

In coastal waters, where rivers bring down sediment which is suspended and stirred up by tidal and wave action, all three factors operate simultaneously; vision is obscured and weakened by the cloud of particles and the illumination is low since the daylight is weakened by the same cause. Sometimes, for example, divers cannot see their own hands. Direct observation is useless under these conditions except for the use of feeling. Obscurity can also be produced by biological obstruction, e.g. plankton. Measurements which have been made show that in the worst conditions the rate of loss of light energy can be as much as 99% per yard and is regularly 50%. Yet coastal waters can be relatively clear, as in the Mediterranean and some parts of Britain.

In the deep ocean the water can be very clear, and the rate of loss of light energy may be as low as 2% per yard. Provided there were adequate illumination, this would permit good visual observation of objects within reasonable distance of the observer, say up to 50 yards. But obviously at great depths, this rate of loss of light energy means that no significant proportion of daylight can penetrate from the surface and, indeed, too little light for human vision reaches a depth of even 700 yards (350 fathoms) in the clearest water.

Of course, artificial illumination can be used, e.g. electric floodlights or searchlights, as on the "Trieste", and valuable observations thus made. But it is certain that this must modify the behaviour of any animal life observed, and thus there is still a limitation in the method. In turbid coastal waters, of course, artificial illumination cannot help much as the water is itself obscure. It is perhaps worth adding that turbid conditions can occur in the deep ocean too, due to the occasional movement of huge amounts of sediments down the slopes of the continental shelves; such movements are called turbidity currents.

3.3   *Indirect use of light*

Even though the direct use of light by human observers has only limited scope, light can still form a valuable basis of observation when used indirectly through photography and television.

Underwater cameras have been developed to a high pitch of perfection. Optically they are little different from ordinary cameras, but mechanically and structurally they have to be somewhat different to remain watertight under great water pressure. When a camera is used with artificial illumination, as it usually has to be, the flash lamp is coupled to the camera (see Fig. 9), and a very useful arrangement for studying the sea-floor and its plant and animal life (as used in the camera developed by the National Institute of Oceanography) is for the flash (and shutter) to be triggered by the impact when the assembly reaches the sea-floor, the lens then being in the correct position to photograph a few square yards of the floor. The disadvantage of the use of artificial illumination which applies to direct human observation—i.e. that the living organisms alter their behaviour in the light—no longer applies, since the duration of the flash is too short for any change to take place. But, of course, the consequence is that only still pictures are taken and animal behaviour cannot be directly observed. Nevertheless, the behaviour can be inferred from still pictures in many cases. Normally the range of objects photographed from the camera is only a yard or two. (See Figs. 10, 11 and 12.)

Underwater television has been developed during the last twenty years, and can give good results in the observation of animal life. The camera can be placed where desired in the water, and the picture observed immediately on the screen on the ship. A cable connection to the ship is necessary. Artificial illumination from floodlights is not necessary in clear shallow water in daylight. Excellent results have been reported in the observation of fish entering a net (see Fig. 13). The system clearly has possibilities in fisheries research.

Underwater ciné cameras, with electric floodlights and a timing mechanism, are available. They can be used to observe animal behaviour, but like underwater television, have the same disadvantage as direct visual methods in that when artificial light is used, it must affect the behaviour being observed.

It is interesting to enquire as to the limits of the possibility of making underwater television or photographic observations by

means of the daylight which penetrates the water. Assuming
the clearest possible conditions and maximum sunshine at the
surface, we find that the theoretical minimum possible illumination at which an observation could possibly be made* if ideal
equipment were available is reached at a depth of the order of
1,400 yards. With the best electronic equipment (camera and
image intensifier) at present achieved, the maximum depth
would be about 800 yards, and in normal oceanic water this
would come down to less than 200 yards. In turbid water the
permissible depth would be negligible. So there is no possible
prospect of making underwater observations without artificial
illumination in most practical circumstances of importance;
the good results which have been demonstrated have not been
obtained under normal operational conditions as known in
Britain, where probably not much fishing takes place in
daylight in clear water of less than 20 fathoms depth.

3.4 *Use of radio waves*

Radio waves and light waves are both examples of electromagnetic waves. Light waves have wavelengths in the range
from about 0·3 to about 0·7 millionth of a metre, whereas
radio waves are of much longer wavelength, say from rather
less than 1 cm. up to nearly 100 km. Between these two lie the
infra-red waves, and with wavelengths shorter than those of
light are the ultra-violet waves, X-rays, and other radiations
known as gamma-rays.

Out of all this vast range of wavelengths it is only the light
waves which show any reasonable penetration of water. In the
previous sections it has been shown what severe limitations even
light has as a means of observation in water. But no other
wavelengths among those mentioned show any comparable
penetration. The lower radio frequencies show up as the best of
the bad lot with an energy loss of around 50% per yard—but

---

* This theoretical minimum illumination is based on the nature of light energy.
Light waves, however continuous they may seem to us, are in fact composed of
tiny particles of energy called photons. At normal levels of illumination, every
square foot of surface receives perhaps a hundred million million million photons
per second. The minimum possible illumination at which observations can be
made is taken to be one photon per second per square foot. Even this, which is
rather optimistic, would fail to detect fish swimming at all fast, and it would give
no directly intelligible picture.

Fig. 2.—Echo-sounder record showing scattering layers of small marine organisms taken off the South Arabian coast. Note the main layer around 120–160 fathoms depth, with layers also around 40 fathoms and close to the surface. The distinct dark segments are shoals of fish, The chart covers a depth of 200 fathoms from the surface (near the top of chart) to the bottom of the chart. The horizontal direction represents the travel of the ship. (*Text page 24*)

(*Courtesy National Institute of Oceanography*)

34

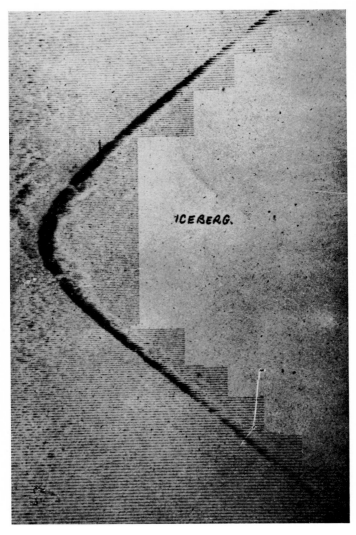

ICEBERG.

Fig. 3.—Sonar record showing a small iceberg passing close to the ship. The beam of the sonar system was horizontal, and was, once the iceberg was detected, kept directed at it as the ship approached it, passed it at quite close range (about 100 yards), and then left it behind. The dark segment is therefore not a profile of a large iceberg, but merely the track of the small iceberg relative to the ship. (In the chart as shown, the distance from ship to iceberg is horizontal, while the vertical scale is effectively just time as the ship steams along.) (*Text page 25*)

(*Courtesy Ministry of Defence, Navy Department*)

Fig. 4.—Diver equipped with acoustic telephone link. The electronic unit is in the small cylinder strapped to the large gas cylinder; the electro-acoustic transducer is just below the small sphere at the top of the unit; the on/off switch is on the diver's belt; and the lead from the electronic unit to the throat microphone and bone-conduction earpiece can also be seen. (*Text page 26*)

(*Courtesy Coastal Radio Ltd.*)

Fig. 5.—Corer about to be dropped in order to obtain a sample (or core) of the sea-bottom; the heavy weight at the top drives it some distance into the bottom. (*Text page 28*)   (*Courtesy National Institute of Oceanography*)

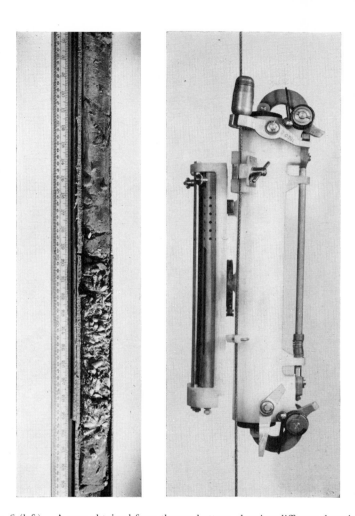

Fig. 6 (left).—A core obtained from the sea-bottom, showing different deposits at different depths. (*Text page 28*)
(*Courtesy National Institute of Oceanography*)

Fig. 7 (right).—Plastic water bottle for taking samples of sea-water at a given depth, with reversing thermometers fitted. Initially the valves at each end are open, but when the messenger weight drops down the wire it closes them and reverses the thermometers; it also releases another weight to operate the next bottle down the wire. (*Text page 28*)
(*Courtesy National Institute of Oceanography*)

Fig. 8.—A vertical plankton net being prepared for use. This is the type standard-
ized for the Indian Ocean Expedition, 1963–4. (*Text page 29*)
(*Courtesy National Institute of Oceanography*)

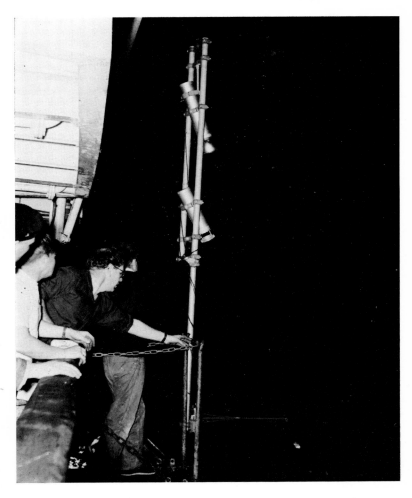

Fig. 9.—The deep-sea camera (developed at the National Institute of Oceano-graphy) being lowered into the water. It is rigged for mid-water photography with a baited trigger in order to photograph squid. The camera is the lower cylinder; the upper one is the lamp for illuminating the scene to be photographed. (*Text page 31*)   (*Courtesy National Institute of Oceanography*)

Fig. 10.—Photograph of a squid obtained by the method shown in Fig. 9. The tentacles are each about 1 foot long and the body about 2 feet. (*Text page 31*) (*Courtesy National Institute of Oceangraphy*)

Fig. 11.—Photograph of sea-floor taken with the underwater camera shown in Fig. 9 (although with a different rig). The area included in the photograph is about 3×4 metres at a depth of 3,900 metres on a seamount on the southern flanks of the Carlsberg Ridge. Boulders are seen on a bedrock of volcanic lava and are rounded by manganese encrustation. (*Text page 31*)
(*Courtesy National Institute of Oceanography*)

42

Fig. 12.—A photograph taken in the sea by a camera mounted on a trawl, showing haddock gathered near the cod-end. Some of the fish are swimming along, keeping pace with the net. (*Text page 31*)
(*Courtesy Marine Laboratories, Aberdeen*)

Fig. 13.—Underwater television picture of fish (mostly haddock) in the cod-end of the trawl. Taken before sunrise using artificial illumination. The object is to show the reaction of the fish to the change from towing to hauling back the net. (*Text page 31*)   (*Courtesy Robert Livingstone, Jr., U.S. Fish & Wildlife Service*)

44

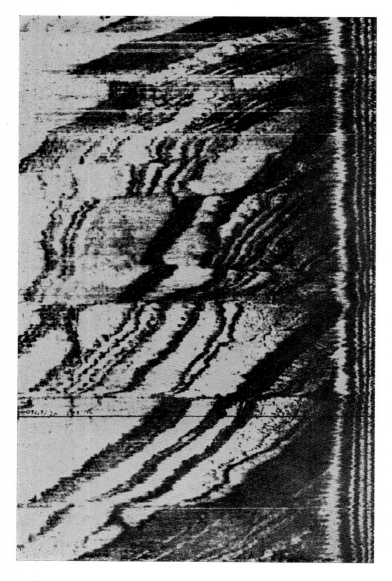

Fig. 15.—Record taken with slanting sonar beam, directed at right-angles to ship's fore-and-aft axis, showing the structure of the sea-bed in terms of roughness, ridges, etc. The sea-bed in this area is largely of rock. The rock ridges produce a strong return so that they appear as darker bands. Fractures in the bed are apparent and the grouping of the ridges on two sides of a fracture sometimes allows identification of corresponding points.
(*Text page 56*)

(*Courtesy National Institute of Oceanography*)

45

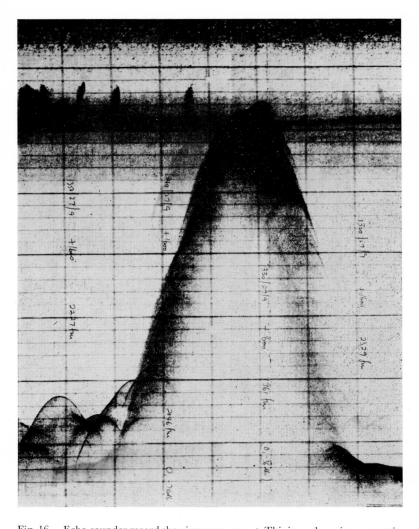

Fig. 16.—Echo-sounder record showing a sea-mount. This is a submarine mountain rising over 3,000 feet above the sea-bottom on each side. For the profile of the sea-mount, the zero of the depth scale must be regarded as offset by 1,600 fathoms above the top of the chart. The scattering layer and fish shoals indicated as apparently at the depth of the peak of the sea-mount are, in fact, in the upper levels of the water; but the various ranges of the scale become overlapped in this method of presentation. (*Text page 56*)

(*Courtesy National Institute of Oceanography*)

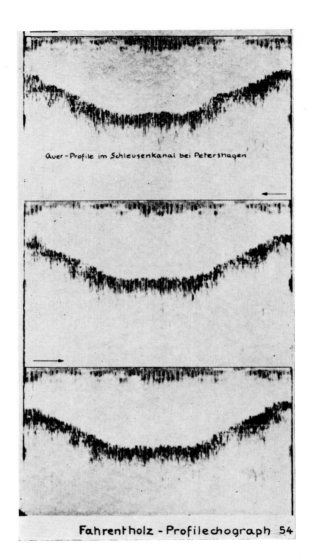

Fig. 17.—Profiles showing three cross-sections of a canal in Germany taken with a multiple echo-sounder device called the Profile Echograph. The survey ship is equipped with outriggers carrying a large number of equally-spaced transducers.

(*Text page 56*)

(*From a paper by S. Fahrentholz: Journal of the British Institution of Radio Engineers, August 1963, by courtesy of the author and the Institution, now the Institution of Electronic & Radio Engineers.*)

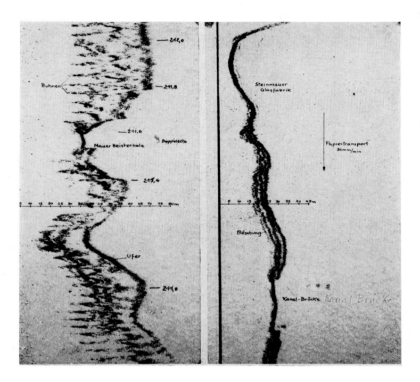

Fig. 18.—Records obtained with a horizontal-beam sonar directed towards the banks of a river. Left: showing reed-covered bank with groynes. Right: showing canal embankment with intervening bridge pier. (*Text page 56*)

(*From a paper by S. Fahrentholz: Journal of the British Institution of Radio Engineers, August 1963, by courtesy of the author and the Institution, now the Institution of Electronic & Radio Engineers.*)

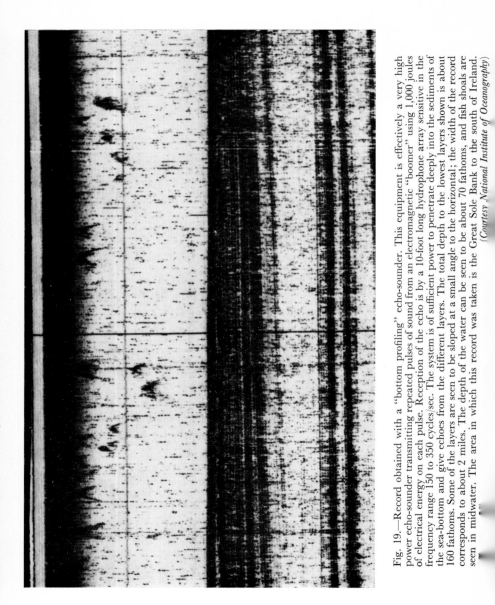

Fig. 19.—Record obtained with a "bottom profiling" echo-sounder. This equipment is effectively a very high power echo-sounder transmitting repeated pulses of sound from an electromagnetic "boomer" using 1,000 joules of electrical energy on each pulse. Reception of the echo is by a 10-foot long hydrophone array sensitive in the frequency range 150 to 350 cycles/sec. The system is of sufficient power to penetrate deeply into the sediments of the sea-bottom and give echoes from the different layers. The total depth to the lowest layers shown is about 160 fathoms. Some of the layers are seen to be sloped at a small angle to the horizontal; the width of the record corresponds to about 2 miles. The depth of the water can be seen to be about 70 fathoms, and fish shoals are seen in midwater. The area in which this record was taken is the Great Sole Bank to the south of Ireland.

(Courtesy National Institute of Oceanography)

that with a wavelength of over 60 miles! There seems to be no possible application in fisheries work for underwater radio waves.

Of course, in the air, things are quite different. Then radio waves generally have much longer ranges of penetration than light waves, as is well known, owing to the absorption and scattering of light energy in clouds and haze.

3.5 *Miscellaneous methods of observation*

It is worth noticing, in passing, that there are often some very simple ways of obtaining information about what goes on underwater. Dr. J. N. Carruthers has invented many such, and one of the most interesting is the jelly bottle. In essence this comprises merely a sealed bottle partly filled with gelatine solution in which a small compass floats. The gelatine is melted by immersing the bottle in hot water, and then the bottle, which is attached by a piece of twine at its mouth to a sinker on the end of a line, is thrown overboard. The sinker lies on the bottom, and the bottle, which is buoyant, takes an inclination dependent on the current. The gelatine sets, and on recovery, the angle of the gelatine surface relative to the wall of the bottle is measured, while the compass, now set in the gelatine, enables the direction of the current to be read.

The jelly bottle has been used to determine the actual shape of the mouth opening of a trawl. A number were fitted around the headline and as the jelly set the inclination of its surface in the bottle recorded the inclination of the headline at that point. From this information the shape shown in Fig. 14 was determined by Mr. G. H. Ellis of Kelvin-Hughes Ltd.

Another useful and elegant, though more complex, device is the instrument for determining the depth of a net or trawl which measures depth by the effect of the water pressure in deflecting a diaphragm. The diaphragm and the fixed plate behind it are used as an electrical condenser or capacitor in an oscillating electronic circuit. Thus as the depth increases the capacitance becomes larger and the frequency of oscillation becomes lower. The frequency generated is relayed to the ship by means of a telemetry link (which may be a cable link but is more conveniently an acoustic link) and there measured and converted to a depth measurement.

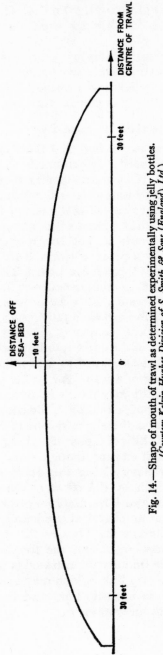

Fig. 14.—Shape of mouth of trawl as determined experimentally using jelly bottles.
(*Courtesy Kelvin-Hughes Division of S. Smith & Sons (England) Ltd.*)

3.6 *Acoustic methods of observation*

We have seen that the basic problem of getting information underwater is to overcome the difficulties due to the relative inaccessibility of the environment. Direct sampling and direct observation, observation by camera or television or special recording instruments, all have a clumsiness and uncertainty much worse than corresponding terrestrial observations and also a much more limited range of observation. Radio waves have been shown to be of no value. So it is not surprising that increasing attention has been given in the last decade or two to the possibilities offered by the use of acoustic waves.

In air we use acoustic* waves for ordinary speech communication between humans and for certain other communication purposes as exemplified by motor-car horns and fire sirens. But we know that the range of such communication is quite limited—normally to only a few yards and exceptionally (as with the fire siren) to a mile or so. By contrast we find that under good conditions light waves have a very great range (of possibly 50 miles or more) and radio waves, in these days of satellite communications, are scarcely severely limited in range at all. We also know that for getting detailed information quickly about things around us we use light waves and our optical system, not only because of the long ranges which are possible, but also because the very short wavelengths of light (less than one millionth of a metre) permit a very high resolution (i.e. a very fine detail) to be obtained. Blind people, who have to rely on acoustic waves for all information from beyond the range of their limbs, are very handicapped. It is true that some species of bat are able to demonstrate a very remarkable ability to explore their surroundings and prey by means of acoustic waves alone and this has led to investigations of the possibility of improving the mobility of blind people by means of more highly developed acoustic equipment than we are provided with naturally. But still acoustic waves remain a "second best".

* Strictly speaking, "acoustic" and "sound" waves are those of frequency within the audible range. But the terms are generally used to cover all waves of this type, irrespective of whether the frequency is audible or not. Another common term is "ultrasonic", but this seems to exclude audible frequencies which are then referred to as "sonic", while frequencies below, say, 200 cycles/sec are referred to as "sub-sonic".

Under water the position is entirely reversed. Radio waves are useless and light waves of very limited value. But acoustic waves can penetrate to relatively great ranges, normally up to a few miles, but in special cases to tens or even hundreds and thousands of miles. The wavelengths which are potentially useful lie in the range, very roughly, from one millimetre (one twenty-fifth of an inch) up to about 50 metres or yards— or in terms of frequency from around 1 megacycle/sec down to about 30 cycles/sec.

Acoustic waves are of a quite different physical nature from light and radio waves. These latter, as we have said before, are examples of electromagnetic waves and they involve electric and magnetic fields. They can therefore propagate (or travel) in a vacuum (as when they come to us from the stars) and when they propagate in a physical medium such as a gas or liquid are subject to losses of energy—relatively slight in clear air and relatively heavy in water. By contrast, acoustic waves are based on the vibration of the actual material of the medium and are recognized as the periodic variation of pressure in the medium. Because of this they cannot propagate at all in a vacuum, and usually propagate well in liquids and solids.

The result of this physical nature of acoustic waves is that the energy losses during the travel of the wave are dependent on the exact composition of the material through which they travel but are lower at low frequencies (i.e. long wavelengths) than at high frequencies. In sea-water, the energy loss is negligible at frequencies as low as 100 c/s, is of the order of 10% per nautical mile at 6 kilocycles/sec, 50% per mile at 15 kc/s, 99% per mile at about 40 kc/s, and 2% per *yard* at about 500 kc/s. These figures are, of course, only rough and vary somewhat with temperature, salinity and other factors. But it will be seen that even at 500 kc/s the energy loss per yard is no more than that of light under the very clearest deep oceanic conditions. The dependence of acoustic waves on the condition of the water is very slight in comparison with that of light waves.

The figures quoted above cannot be used alone to calculate the possible range of observation obtainable with acoustic waves. As will be indicated in more detail later, the matter is really quite complicated. But it is clear that acoustic waves have some very real advantages.

We must now consider the various ways in which wave energy may be used to obtain information. In using light, in everyday life, we normally have the scene we want to examine already illuminated by daylight or artificially illuminated from a local source (i.e. lamp). We are able to examine the whole cross-section of our field of view in detail because the optical system of our eye is able to resolve the detail, and give a sufficient number of distinct pieces of information about the illumination of the scene to the nerves of the retina to enable our brain to interpret the scene. We can think of this crudely in terms of an ordinary "half-tone" illustration in a book or newspaper, in which the picture is made up of a very large number of dots. The size, or blackness, of each gives information about the illumination of that particular small element of the picture. The quality of a half-tone picture—i.e. the amount of information or detail it gives—is proportional to the number of dots by which it is represented. This is what we mean by "resolution" or "resolving the detail". So the amount of information we can get is dependent on the fineness of the focus which the lens of the eye can produce on the retina (and also on the density of optical nerves, of course). This is proportional to the dimensions of the lens (assuming it is properly corrected optically) measured in units of wavelength of the light. Very roughly the effective number of elements of resolution (or effective "dots") which a lens can produce is equal to four times the area of the lens in square wavelengths. It is thus perfectly easy to have a thousand millions of elements of resolution with an optical lens.

Now although acoustic waves are different from light waves in their mechanism, they behave in exactly the same way as far as the concept of resolution is concerned. So to get the same sort of effect as that described above for light pictures we should need firstly to provide a continuous and powerful "insonification" corresponding to the illumination from the sun or a lamp, and secondly to provide an acoustic lens, focusing mirror, or other receiver which has a linear dimension of the order of ten thousand wavelengths. The first requirement is feasible, but the second is not. We have seen that the highest useable frequency, where the energy loss per yard is about 2% is around 500 kc/s—i.e. a wavelength of about 3 millimetres.

It is just conceivable that one might go to a wavelength of 1 mm. for special short-range work. But this wavelength is over a thousand times that of light, and to obtain the sort of resolution asked for, a lens (or other receiver) of say 50-feet diameter would be needed—perhaps not impossible, but certainly not practicable. So an acoustic system of this type would have to make do with a resolution much inferior to what we are used to having visually. No really successful acoustic system of this type has yet been produced.

Another way in which we are used to obtaining information visually is to use light actually emitted by the object we are looking at. Looking down at a town at night from a hill or an aircraft we obtain an interpretable picture of this type. The resolution of detail on which our recognition of the scene depends requires the same optical resolution as for the externally-illuminated scene.

Is there any acoustic equivalent to this underwater? Certainly there is no exact equivalent, and even if there were it would not be so useful as we would still depend on having such a large receiver to get the desired resolution. The sea-bottom itself and the rocks on it do not emit any acoustic energy except in the special case of shingle being rolled about by a tidal current. But fish do, in general, emit sounds and it is possible to detect and recognize these, not in a manner corresponding to visual observations, but by analyzing the distribution of sound energy over the range of frequencies (or pitch) and its variation with time, just as the ear analyzes and permits the brain to recognize human speech and other terrestial sounds. There is a good deal of information on the sounds emitted by fish and other marine organisms such as shrimps, and they can be used by fishermen. Apparently the Japanese use this "listening" or "passive" acoustic method of fish detection, and there seem to be some noisy fish in American waters. Of course, the listening is done via an electro-acoustic transducer (or hydrophone) in the water and an amplifier.

Having concluded that the two methods of observation which are used visually are not very promising for use underwater with acoustic waves, we turn to the method which so far has given the most outstanding results: the method of *echo-location*. This method is usable with acoustic or electromagnetic waves in air; in the former case we have the natural system used by bats and the man-made system being developed for the guidance of blind people, and in the electromagnetic case we have the well-known radar. Underwater, only the acoustic echo-location system is workable; this is the system usually called sonar (or formerly asdic). In its simplest concept, a short pulse, or "ping", of acoustic energy is transmitted from the equipment and travels out through the water. Some of this energy is reflected, or echoed, back by any object in the water, and if this echo-pulse can be detected, then the time delay between the transmission of the pulse and the reception of the echo is a measure of the distance of the object. If the transmission can be confined to a narrow angle, then this indicates the direction of the object. We notice immediately that this method of observation has one important potential advantage over the ordinary visual observation: distance is measured accurately as well as the position in terms of angle or bearing.

The resolution in a visual system is, of course, the resolution in bearing. The resolution of an echo-location system in bearing is dependent on having a narrow sound beam on transmission and/or reception. The requirement of the lens system that it should have dimensions large compared with the wavelength is replaced in the sonar by the requirement that the transducers (which are the devices which convert electrical energy into acoustical energy and vice versa and are used to transmit and receive the acoustical signal) should have dimensions equally large compared with the wavelength for the same resolution to be obtained. But since in the sonar system we have a high degree of resolution in range (i.e. an accurate separation of objects at different distances) we can afford to sacrifice a good deal of angular resolution. Thus a comparatively compact sonar equipment can give a very large amount of information regarding what is in the water.

Sonar is, indeed, the most valuable of methods of under-water observation for many important purposes, and as its design and development becomes more and more refined, its range of applications will clearly expand. Sonar is not new; it was developed in the First World War for detecting sub-marines. But it has emerged into widespread use in the civil fields, such as those described earlier, only in the last two decades. A lot has still to be learned about its civil potentialities.

It should be mentioned here that sonar can be used for quite a number of needs outlined earlier. Its use in fisheries work is considered in detail in a companion volume (The Buckland Lectures, 1966: "Sonar in Fisheries"). It is a valuable means of observation of the sea-bottom, showing its roughness and surface features, sand-waves, etc. (see Fig. 15). Its use in navigation is well known and has already been mentioned; knowledge of the ocean depths, of the continental slopes and submarine canyons, of sea-mounts (see Fig. 16) and so forth has been obtained with vertical sonars (or echo-sounders). Silting of harbours and rivers is detected with sonar (see Figs. 17 and 18). A great deal of the knowledge of the sediments and rocks under the sea is obtained using what is effectively a low-frequency high-power sonar, in other words the equipment used for "seismic shooting" and "bottom profiling". (See Fig. 19).

In earlier sections a good deal has been made of the objection to the use of artificial illumination to aid optical observation because of its effect in modifying the behaviour of the animal life being observed. It might be thought that the use of active, or pinging, sonar would be open to the corresponding objection that the sound-waves might affect behaviour. Certainly fish have hearing mechanisms, but it is thought that the sound levels are too low and often the frequencies used are too high for this objection to be valid. There is no observational evidence of it being valid, either, but the matter certainly requires further investigation.

Chapter 2

Acoustic waves, beams and echoes

1 Introduction

Having now introduced acoustic systems of underwater observation as those with the greatest potentialities for rapid, convenient, accurate and remote gathering of information, we must now proceed to a discussion of the fundamental physical and theoretical ideas on which the design of systems has to be based. Most of the basic knowledge of acoustic waves is quite old, having been thoroughly set out in mathematical and experimental terms by Lord Rayleigh in his famous treatise "The Theory of Sound" in 1877. This book is still kept in print and is still very valuable as a text-book of a rather advanced nature. By contrast, much of the basic knowledge of the "system" aspects of sonar, which we shall touch on in a later chapter, is really quite recent, much of it having been developed by electrical engineers during the last two or three decades, and introduced into design only even more recently.

In this chapter we consider the classical ideas of acoustic waves, in so far as they are relevant to sonar.

2 Acoustic waves

Acoustic waves arise most frequently through the mechanical vibration of some surface, usually a stiff or rigid one. Consider a sealed box placed in the water; one side of it is made to vibrate to and fro by some mechanism inside the box. When the side moves outwards, it exerts a pressure on the water, and in the immediate vicinity, the particles of which the water can be considered to be composed move correspondingly. This causes a pressure to be exerted on particles a little further away and they move forward too. This process continues, and the pressure is gradually transmitted forward. But the side of the box soon starts to move backward, and a negative pressure is exerted on the water (or, in other words, the normal pressure in the water due to its weight and the pressure of the atmosphere above it—the hydrostatic pressure—is reduced). The particles move back past their original position, and this effect too is gradually transmitted forward. The reversals then continue so long as the side of the box is vibrated. At a distant point in the water the oscillations of pressure (and of the water particles) lag behind those at the box, since it has taken time for the pressures and movements to be transmitted onwards.

2.1 *Simple waves*

Now the simplest type of vibration which can be produced is that known as simple harmonic motion. This is the motion of the surface (or side of the box) which arises if a crank is rotated at a constant speed, and the crank pin engages in a slot in a bracket fixed to the side of the box, as shown in Fig. 20. The displacement of the surface changes smoothly, without any sudden changes of speed, and the graph of displacement as a function of time is derived in Fig. 20 also. This is the well-known sinusoidal curve. If the instant corresponding to the state of affairs shown in the upper drawing is taken as the zero point of time, and at this instant the crank arm is making an angle θ radians to the vertical, then the displacement of the surface from its mean position at any time t is expressed mathematically as

$$\xi = \xi_{max} \sin (2\pi ft + \theta) \qquad \ldots \quad (1)$$

where the inelegant Greek symbol Xi (ξ) is the standard symbol for displacement, ξ_{max} is the maximum displacement corresponding to the length of the crank, and f is the frequency of the vibration, i.e. the rate at which the surface moves to and fro, measured in cycles per second. The Greek symbol Pi (π) is used in its usual meaning of the ratio of the circumference to the diameter of a circle. Angles are measured in radians; there are 2π radians in a complete rotation, otherwise called 360 degrees. Thus one radian is approximately 57·3 degrees.

Consideration of the physical problem shows us that the acoustic pressure developed by the vibrating surface is greatest when the displacement passes through zero and that the particle velocity (i.e. the actual velocity with which any particle of water actually moves at any instant due to the vibration) is also greatest then. The variation of acoustic

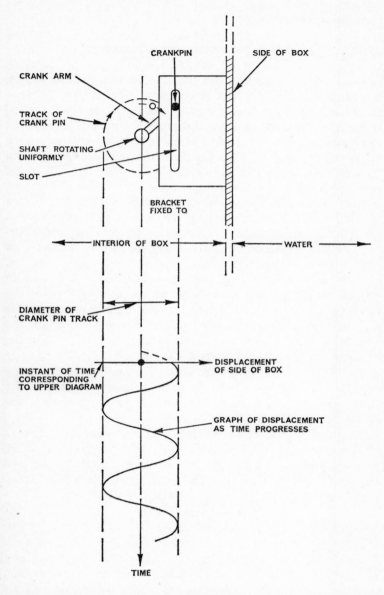

Fig. 20.—Showing the generation of simple harmonic motion and a sinusoidal waveform.

pressure (p) with time is then given by a cosine relation instead of a sine relation:
$$p = p_{max} \cos (2\pi ft + \theta) \qquad \ldots \ (2)$$
and the variation of particle velocity (u) is similarly
$$u = u_{max} \cos (2\pi ft + \theta) \qquad \ldots \ (3)$$
We are here assuming that the vibrating surface (as implied by the drawing in Fig. 20) is of large extent, that is to say that it extends a very large number of wavelengths in both surface dimensions and that we are considering the part of the surface near its centre, and the region of space not many wavelengths away from the surface. The way the acoustic effect spreads into space is then indicated schematically in Fig. 21. The lines drawn parallel to the vibrating surface are taken to represent layers of water that are equally spaced apart when the surface is not vibrating. Thus when they are closer together we have a region of high pressure, or positive acoustic pressure, and when they are further apart we have a region of low pressure, or negative acoustic pressure. This is shown on the graph below. It is easy to see from Fig. 21 that, as stated above, the acoustic pressure is maximum (positively or negatively) when the displacement is zero, and zero when the displacement is maximum, at all stages in the travel of the wave through the water. One must picture the lines vibrating to and fro, like the vibrating surface, and it is then easy to see that the particle velocity follows the pressure exactly. (To simplify the language we shall henceforth call the acoustic pressure—which is the excess pressure over the hydrostatic pressure—just "the pressure").

The graph in Fig. 21 shows clearly why this acoustic effect is called a wave. If x is the distance from the mean position of the vibrating surface, and the distance between successive peaks of pressure—which is known as the wavelength—is λ (the Greek letter Lambda), then the wave may be written
$$p = p_{max} \cos (2\pi/\lambda)x \qquad \ldots \ (4)$$
and similarly for the particle velocity u. But this is the expression for the wave at the instant for which the diagram is drawn. At any subsequent instant the vibrating surface will be in a different part of its cycle of vibration, and the displacements, pressures and particle velocities all along the x-axis will be different. The wave will have moved forward. At different

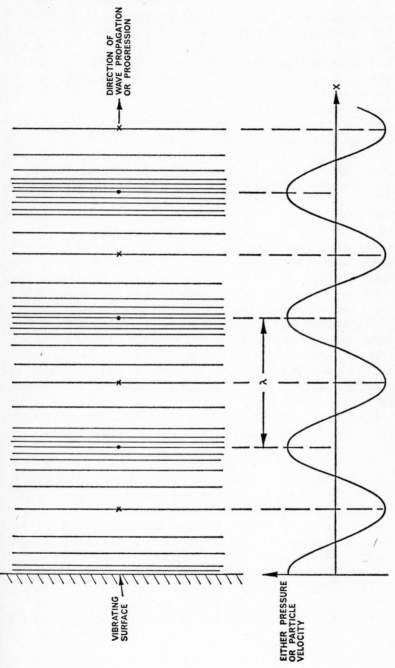

Fig. 21.—The acoustic wave in the water; vibrating surface very large.

points in the water, the pressure and particle velocity will vary
with time according to the equations (2) and (3), but with
different origins on the time-scale. We thus have to picture the
wave as something which progresses in both time and space.
The equations (2) and (4) each tell us part of the story, but the
two have to be combined to tell us it all. The full statement of
the wave equation (of pressure) is thus

$$p = p_{max} \cos [2\pi f t + \theta - (2\pi/\lambda)x] \qquad \dots \quad (5)$$

We have a minus sign for the space term because the time-wave
at any point further along the x-axis corresponds to an earlier
time origin. Equation (5) tells us what the pressure will be for
any particular point in space at any given instant of time.

2.2   *Spherical or spreading waves*

In the above discussion we have assumed that the vibrating
surface is of very large extent—longer than any distance we are
considering—and this is clearly an unrealistic assumption,
made only for convenience. In practice the vibrating surface
must be considered to be of relatively small size, usually just a
few wavelengths at most. To take the other extreme, consider
for a moment that the vibrating surface is very small compared
with the wavelength. Then the situation is now as shown
schematically in Fig. 22. The lines of equal pressure now tend
to be circles centred on the vibrating source. Of course, in
making a diagram we are considering only what is happening
in one particular plane, and the lines of equal pressure really
represent spherical surfaces of equal pressure. In the previous
case—Fig. 21—we had what are called "plane waves"; we
now have "spherical waves".

Now very near the small source the wave behaviour is
complicated, as may readily be imagined, and among other
things the pressure and particle velocity do not exactly
correspond as they did with the plane wave. But a little further
away (say roughly a wavelength away) the wave motion
becomes normal. But one most important point must now be
noticed. With the spherical wave, the cross-sectional area over
which the acoustic power is spread increases as we move outwards from the source, according to the square of the distance x.
Thus the power flow per unit cross-sectional area, which is
called the acoustic "intensity", I, diminishes as given by the

well-known "inverse-square law", i.e. $1/x^2$. Thus both pressure and particle velocity diminish as x increases, as indicated on the graph in Fig. 22.

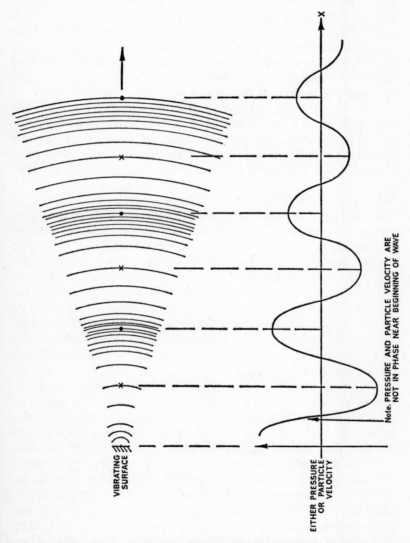

Fig. 22.—The acoustic wave in the water; vibrating surface very small.

Now pressure and particle velocity are closely analogous to voltage and current in electric circuits, and the acoustic intensity corresponds to power. Indeed, I is the product of the r.m.s. pressure and particle velocity just as electric power is the product of r.m.s. voltage and current (r.m.s., or "root-mean-square", is the effective value over a whole cycle of the wave). Therefore since I diminishes with distance x according to $1/x^2$, both pressure and particle velocity diminish according to $1/x$. The wave equation for a spherical wave, at a point not too near the surface, is therefore

$$p = (p_{max}/x) \cos [2\pi ft + \theta - (2\pi/\lambda)x] \quad \dots \quad (6)$$

In passing, it is worth noting that the electrical analogy can be taken further, and that the ratio of pressure to particle velocity (i.e. p/u) is called the acoustic impedance or resistance of the water, just as Ohm's Law gives $V/I = Z$ or R in electric circuits.

2.3   *Decibels and losses*

We shall need to use later a very important unit of measurement—the decibel. This is not something like inches or metres, or seconds or pounds, which measure actual quantities. The decibel measures a change or ratio on a logarithmic basis. If the acoustic power flow per square metre, or intensity, at one point is one-tenth of that at a point nearer the source, we say that there is a diminution of intensity of 10 decibels or 10 dB. If the power at one point is one-hundredth (or one-thousandth) of that at the other, the diminution is 20 dB (or 30 dB) and so on. Actually the number of decibels is ten times the logarithm of the power ratio, i.e. $10 \log_{10}(P_1/P_2)$, where P_1 is the larger power. Thus a power diminution of 2: 1 is 3 dB, and a pressure diminution of 2: 1 is 6 dB (since power is proportional to the square of pressure). Referring to the spherical waves and the inverse-square law, it is common to say that the "spreading loss" is 6 dB per doubling of distance.

There are other sources of loss when a wave propagates through water. These losses (which have been mentioned earlier in the review of methods of underwater observation in Chapter 1) depend on a number of factors, including the temperature and the amount of dissolved salts, and they represent a conversion of acoustic energy into heat. They depend very much on the frequency of the vibration. These losses are different from spreading loss in that they are represented by a given number of decibels per unit distance (and not per doubling of distance). Some typical curves are given in

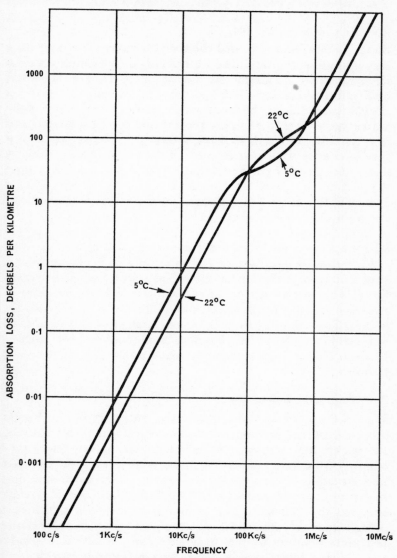

Fig. 23.—Absorption loss in sea-water at different frequencies.

Fig. 23 to show the dependence of these "absorption" losses on frequency and temperature. The figures are very variable; they depend greatly on circumstances. We shall return to these losses when considering the design of a sonar system later.

2.4 *Velocity of propagation*

So far we have not discussed the speed with which the acoustic wave progresses through the water. This is something which is determined by the fundamental elastic properties of the water, and is the same for all frequencies of vibration but varies slightly according to the temperature, salinity, and depth of the water concerned. It is usually represented by the symbol c, and is of the order of a mile or 1,500 metres per second. (In air it is less than a quarter of this; and, of course, it is very slow by comparison with light and radio waves, which travel around 200,000 times faster.) But once knowing the velocity c, and given the frequency f of the signal from the source, we see that the wavelength λ has to be

$$\lambda = c/f, \qquad \ldots \quad (7)$$

where the units of distance are the same for λ and c.

We have discussed waves and vibrations so far in terms of a simple harmonic motion or sinusoidal (or cosinusoidal) waveform. This is indeed the most elementary form possible; it contains only the one frequency, and if this were audible would be heard as a single pure note or tone and we would be able to estimate its pitch. In practice, real sounds are usually "complex", i.e. they contain a mixture of waves of different frequencies.

3   Acoustic beams

We have up till now considered the radiation from a single vibrating surface or "source" and have examined its nature in the water only a very short distance (i.e. only a few wavelengths) from the source. To make further progress towards understanding sonar systems, we must consider more than one source in the same region, and the effects which occur in what is called the "far-field", i.e. that region which is sufficiently distant from the sources for all lines joining a particular point in it to the various sources to be effectively parallel. It is only the far field which has to be considered in most sonar work.

3.1 *Interference of two waves*

Consider two small equal vibrating surfaces or sources as shown at A and B in Fig. 24 and points X_A and X_B in the far-field the lines from which to A and B are at right-angles to the line joining A and B together. Now X_A and X_B are really intended to represent one and the same point, but they have been shown separately because, firstly, it is not practicable to make the distances AX_A and BX_B on the diagram extremely large compared with the distance AB, although we have specified this to be the real condition we are referring to; and secondly, we require to show the waves from A and B separately. So we shall talk about the "point" X, although in the diagram it is represented by two points. Then we can think of the acoustic wave effect at X, in terms of time and space, separately for each source. If we consider the distribution of acoustic pressure at any instant of time along the line from A due to A acting alone, it has the sinusoidal curve as shown on the "distance" axis; but if we consider the variation of pressure with time at X due to A acting alone, this has the sinusoidal curve shown in the upper graph "A" on the "time" axis. Similarly if we consider the effect of B acting alone, we have the other spatial and time curves shown. If both sources are acting together and are driven in synchronism as indicated, then the total acoustic effect at X is just the sum of the two, and as the two effects are identical, the resultant total effect is just double, as shown for the time graph.

Now consider a different "point" Y in the far-field (i.e. Y_A and Y_B corresponding to X_A and X_B), where the line from Y to the sources is now not at right-angles to the line joining A and B. Assume the distance BY is the same as BX. Then the spatial and time curves of pressure are the same as before, as indicated in the diagram. But due to the changed angle, the distance AY is not equal to BY, but exceeds it by an amount AC. This means that the wave travelling from A to Y has this much further to travel, and relative to the particular instant of time for which the spatial waves at Y are drawn, the wave received at Y from A must have left A earlier than that from B left B by an amount of time corresponding to the travel time over the distance AC. Now in the diagram the angle of AY relative to AX has been chosen so that AC is one half-wavelength, so that

68   *Underwater observations using sonar*

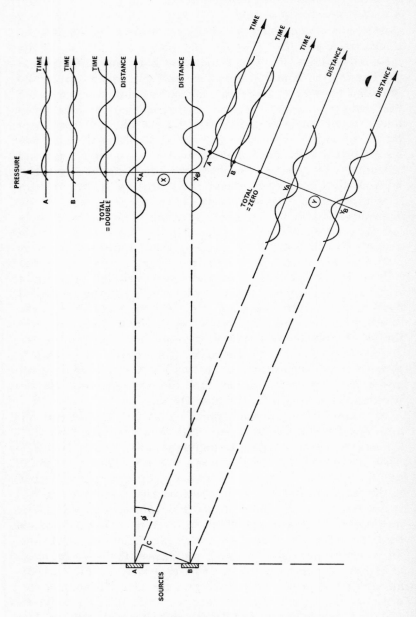

Fig. 24.—Illustrating directional effects with two sources.

the spatial and time waves at Y are, for source A, one half-wavelength behind those for source B. At any instant of time, therefore, the two waves are exactly equal but opposite, and so cancel out entirely, leaving no resultant acoustic effect at Y.

At points in the far-field intermediate between the lines joining the sources to X and Y the acoustic effect is obviously intermediate between the double pressure of X and the zero of Y. At points making a greater angle the waves do not remain cancelled out completely; and, indeed, it can readily be seen that the resultant response oscillates as the angle is steadily increased, there being positions where the maximum occurs and others where zero occurs. This is the most elementary directional effect possible, and the (complete or partial) cancelling of waves is called "interference".

3.2 *Phase angles*

We must now introduce the term "phase" or "phase angle". In discussing the generation of acoustic waves by means of a vibrating surface driven by a crank, as in Fig. 20, we took account of the position of the crank at the time chosen for reference, i.e. $t = 0$, by calling the angle between the crank and the vertical by the symbol θ. This symbol then occurred in all the equations of the wave, and determined thereafter the height of the wave graph at $t = 0$. The angle θ is called the phase angle of the wave. Since the choice of time reference is arbitrary, θ is arbitrary at this stage.

Now suppose we have two sources as in Fig. 24. In considering the interference of the waves from these sources we assumed they were driven in synchronism, by which we meant they both had the same frequency and the same phase angle θ. But if they had had different angles, say θ_A and θ_B respectively, then at all points where the waves in Fig. 24 are identical the new waves would be different because they have different starting values at $t = 0$. From this it follows that the directions in which maximum and zero resultant pressures occur are different. This is because the sources had a "phase difference" of $\theta_A - \theta_B$.

The concept of phase is extended also to the waves themselves. Referring again to Fig. 24, we notice that, even though the sources in the case illustrated had the same phase, the

waves at Y have different values at any reference time due to
the different travel distances from the sources. The waves are
said to have a phase difference between them, and this is
measured by the angular difference between two cranks which
are imagined to be generating them at Y. In the case illustrated,
the waves at Y are exactly of opposite phase, and the phase
difference between them is π radians or 180 degrees.

The phase of a wave changes as it progresses through the
water. Relative to any particular instant of time, the wave at
two points at different distances from a single source has the
same variation with time except for having a different phase
at the two points. If the distance between the points (assumed
both to be on the same line from the source) is x_1 then the
phase difference is $(2\pi/\lambda)x_1$ radians. A phase difference
obtained in this way as a result of transmission or progression
of a wave is often called a "phase-shift". Waves which are
different in phase by any multiple of 2π radians (or 360 degrees)
cannot be distinguished when they are continuous.

3.3   *Interference of several waves*

Although we discussed the interference of two waves previously,
the same kind of thing happens when there are more than two
waves. Even the complete cancellation of several waves to give
a zero resultant is possible if the waves have particular relation-
ships. This is illustrated in Fig. 25 where five waves are shown
with equal peak pressures and phase differences between
adjacent waves of $2\pi/5$ radians or 72 degrees. These waves
add up to zero at all points in time and if the drawing is done
accurately enough this should be readily checked by inspection.
To assist the visualization of the phase differences, crank
positions (for $t = 0$) have been shown on the left for five
sources generating the five waves; but the same effect would,
of course, be obtained if the five sources were identical and the
phase differences were produced by different travel times in the
water.

Actually the notional crank-position diagrams are very useful
for representing the phases of waves. If we make the length of
the crank proportional to the peak pressure (or "amplitude")
of the wave, then the line representing the crank position at
$t = 0$ is called a "phasor". When the waves are added

together, their resultant amplitude is given by the resultant phasor. Drawing all phasors together, as at the bottom left in Fig. 25, we see that they cancel out completely. For example,

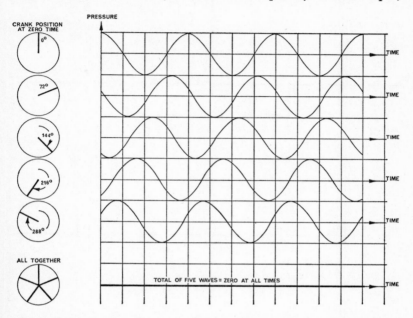

Fig. 25.—Showing that five waves with equal phase differences of 72 degrees cancel out.

if the five phasors were five ropes all joined together at the one point, and all were pulled with equal force, then there would be no movement of the junction point because there would be no resultant force on it.

3.4 Radiation from arrays of sources

When several sources are used together at the same frequency and in a fixed configuration they are called an "array" of sources. The simplest possible array is a pair of sources as used previously, and as shown again at (a) in Fig. 26. Arrays are used to produce deliberate directional effects. For any plane in which the two sources lie, the directional effect may be plotted as the variation of the resultant peak amplitude of the wave at a fixed distance from the point midway between the sources, as

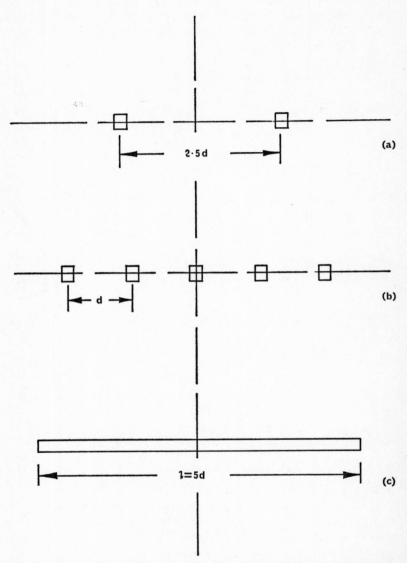

Fig. 26.—Three kinds of line array of sources: (a) two-element array, (b) five-element array, (c) continuous array.

the direction is rotated through 180 degrees on each side of the line at right-angles to the line of the sources. Since this graph is the same, except for the amplitude scale, at all distances in the far-field, it is usual to plot it with an arbitrary amplitude scale and to call it the "directional pattern" of the array. The directional pattern for the "two-element" array of Fig. 26 (a) is shown at (a) in Fig. 27 and is the simple alternation of maxima and zeros as previously discussed. Alternate maxima are of opposite sign, however, indicating a reversal of phase of the wave.

No absolute angular scale has been indicated in Fig. 27. This cannot be done until we define the spacing of the sources in terms of wavelength. For convenience of comparison with other results, we have called this spacing, in this case, $2.5d$. Consideration of Fig. 24 shows that the first zero on each side of the central maximum occurs when the directional angle φ (the Greek symbol Phi) is such as to make AC equal to one half-wavelength. Since the angle ABC also is φ, then AC = AB.sin φ and this is required to be $\lambda/2$ for the first zero. Thus, since AB = $2.5d$ in our case, the first zero occurs when sin $\varphi = \lambda/5d$.

It is most convenient to plot the diagram in terms of sin φ. On this basis the first zeros are shown on the angular scale at sin $\varphi = \lambda/5d$, and subsequent zeros at odd multiples of this.

If now we specify the spacing in terms of wavelength we can draw the directional response in terms of real angles. For example, if $d = \lambda$, then the positions P and Q on the directional scale correspond to sin $\varphi = -1$ and 1 respectively, or $\varphi = -\pi/2$ and $\pi/2$ radians (-90 and 90 degrees) respectively. At this stage we may draw the directional response in what is called "polar" form, as shown in Fig. 28 (a). Here the magnitude of the relative response is indicated by the distance of any point on the graph from the centre, or "origin", and the response is drawn in its correct angular position. Patterns of this kind give a very easily appreciated picture of the response, although it is not very convenient—nor usually necessary—to indicate the difference between positive and negative responses. This is a matter of importance only in some rather advanced types of sonar which we shall not be discussing here.

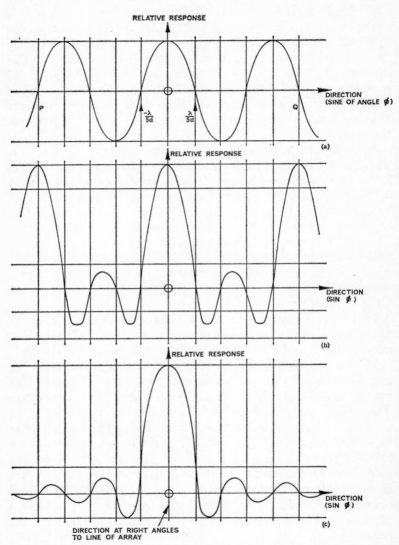

Fig. 27.—Directional responses of arrays: (a) two-element, (b) five-element, (c) continuous.

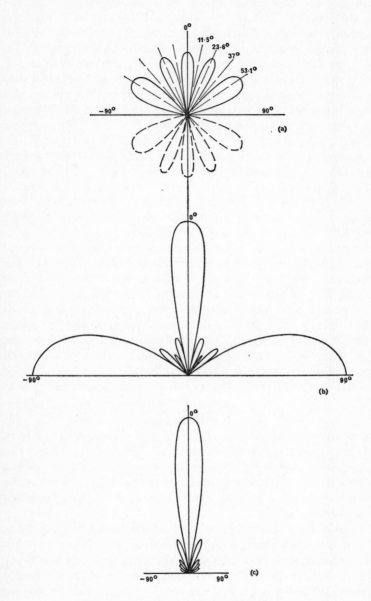

Fig. 28.—Directional responses in polar form.

Clearly the directional effects of a two-element array are not very useful. But if we make a five-element array, for example, as shown in Fig. 26 (b), matters improve considerably. The directional response in terms of sin φ is shown at (b) in Fig. 27 and for $d = \lambda$ again, the polar response is shown at (b) in Fig. 28. We see at once that some of the maximum responses are now quite small, and we have a distinct "beam" in the central position. Unfortunately there are other large beams also, although these would disappear if the spacing d were reduced somewhat—but then the main beam would be broadened. The zero responses in between the various maxima occur through cancellation of five waves with suitable equal phase differences, as shown previously in Fig. 25. If desired, a diagram like that of Fig. 24 could be constructed for five sources in order to make the matter even clearer, but it would really be too complicated to be worthwhile.

Increasing the number of sources and reducing their spacing correspondingly would reduce the various beams other than the main ones, and indeed would eliminate the undesirable large beams. The extreme case is where the array is no longer an array of separate sources but is a long continuous source as shown at (c) in Fig. 26. The directional response then becomes as shown at (c) in Fig. 27, and for a length $l = 5d = 5\lambda$ the polar response is as shown at (c) in Fig. 28. Here the pattern consists of one main beam and a number of "minor lobes". This directional pattern is usually expressed in mathematical form as

$$D = \frac{\sin\left[(\pi l/\lambda)\sin\varphi\right]}{(\pi l/\lambda)\sin\varphi} \qquad \dots \quad (8)$$

and is often referred to as the $(\sin x)/x$ response or pattern. This is a very desirable form of pattern, but the minor lobes can be made even smaller (at the expense of some widening of the main beam) if the array is equivalent to a line of sources the strength of which is greatest at the centre, diminishing towards the end of the array.

We have here considered an array of elements forming a line and the directional patterns are those in a plane containing this line. In a plane perpendicular to the line, the response is the same in all directions. In practice, directionality is usually required in both axes, and so an array is used which covers an area—usually a flat square, rectangular or circle.

The significance of the spacing of the elements in a non-continuous array has already been seen to be important. The graphs of response plotted as in Fig. 27 are quite general and do not assume any particular numerical value of λ/d. But once numbers are put in, the effective range of the curves is limited by the fact that the real angular range is confined to -90 to $+90$ degrees or -180 to $+180$ degrees. It can be seen therefore that the choice of element spacing is important. Whether the real angular range is half a circle or a full circle depends on whether the sources can radiate backwards or not. If they are mounted in a large sheet, or "baffle"—often the hull of a ship can act in this way—then the range of angles is -90 to $+90$ degrees. In this case, an element spacing somewhat less than one wavelength causes the pattern to have only one main beam, and so this array is for many practical purposes as good as a continuous array.

Sonar beams are formed in this way, by using a transducer (i.e. a device for converting electrical energy into acoustic energy) of large surface area or an array of smaller transducers. It will be clear from what has been said above that the narrowness of the beam depends on the largeness of the transducer or array as measured in units of wavelength. The width of a beam is usually measured as the angular difference between the two directions at which the response is 3 dB below the peak response, i.e. at which the power response is one-half, or the pressure response is $1/\sqrt{2}$ or $0\cdot707$, times the peak. On this basis the array of length 5λ we see has a beam width of about 13 degrees; to obtain a beam of only 1 degree the length would have to be about 60λ. At 50 kc/s the wavelength is approximately 3 cm., so that to obtain a beam width of 1 degree at this frequency the corresponding array dimension has to be about 180 cm. or nearly 6 feet.

3.5 *Directional reception*

If it is required to receive an acoustic signal from a distant source (i.e. from a source in the far-field of the receiver) or the echo-signal reflected from a distant fish or other object in the water, then an array of receiving elements may be used to obtain a directional effect just as on transmission. The elements will be electro-acoustic transducers. Suppose two are arranged

in the same positions as the sources A and B in Fig. 24. Consider
first a wave arriving along the direction at right-angles to the
line joining A and B. Since it comes from the far-field, the
radius of curvature of the wave will be very large when it
reaches the receiver, and since A and B are quite close together
in comparison with the distance the wave has travelled, we
may assume the wave is a plane wave as far as reception is
concerned. The wave received at A and B is the same; it has
travelled exactly the same distance and is therefore of the same
phase at the two receivers. The electrical signal waves to which
the acoustic wave is converted have therefore no phase
difference, and if added together will give double the voltage of
each separately.

Now suppose the wave comes from the direction shown as
making an angle φ to the previous direction. Here AC is a
half-wavelength, so the wave arriving at A has to travel a half-
wavelength further than that arriving at B. The electrical
output signal waves are therefore exactly of opposite phase and,
when added together, cancel out. So the directional effect on
reception is the same as on transmission. Following the same
kind of argument through for an array of five or any other
number of receiving elements, we quickly see that directional
effects are obtained on reception which are identical to those
obtained on transmission. Just as on transmission the acoustic
energy can be concentrated into a beam, so on reception the
directions in which the receiver has sensitivity can be concentrated into what is often loosely called a receiving beam.
Indeed, in sonar systems, the same transducer or array of
transducer elements is often used for both transmission and
reception.

4   Reflection and refraction of acoustic waves, and echo-formation

We have so far discussed acoustic waves as though they were in
a uniform medium of infinite extent. But in reality the water is
bounded by air at the surface and by solid material at the
sea-bottom. Other discontinuities also occur, such as breakwaters, ships, fish and so on. So we must consider what
happens when an acoustic wave meets such a boundary or
discontinuity.

4.1 *Reflection and refraction at a smooth plane boundary*

Consider first a smooth boundary of very great extent between two fluid media, such as the sea-surface when calm. Fig. 29

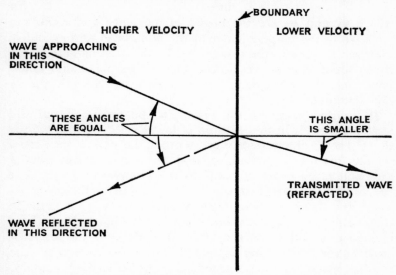

Fig. 29.—Showing reflection and refraction at a boundary between regions having different sound velocities.

indicates such a boundary by a thick vertical line. If an acoustic wave from a distant source (i.e. a plane wave) approaches this boundary at an angle, as shown, then its energy is divided at the boundary, one part being reflected and the other part being transmitted onwards. The part that is reflected forms a wave with the same plane wave character as the arriving (or "incident") wave but with a new direction as shown. The angles are usually referred to the line perpendicular to the boundary and then the angle of reflection is equal to the angle of incidence. This is, of course, exactly the same law as applies to light waves at a mirror. The part of the wave energy which is transmitted through the boundary proceeds in a new direction. It is said to be "refracted". The relationship between the angles of incidence and refraction depends on the ratio of the acoustic wave velocities in the two media; if the second medium has a lower velocity, as shown in the diagram, then

the angle of refraction is smaller than the angle of incidence.
Mathematically this relationship is expressed by Snell's Law:

$$\frac{\sin \varphi_1}{\sin \varphi_2} = \frac{c_1}{c_2} \qquad \qquad \dots \quad (9)$$

where φ_1 and φ_2 are the angles of incidence and refraction
(relative to the perpendicular to the boundary) and c_1 and c_2
are the velocities in the two media. In the limiting case where
the incident wave arrives from a direction perpendicular to the
boundary, the reflected and refracted waves are both also in
this direction.

If we now consider the system to be reversed, and the
incident wave is in the medium of lower velocity, then we see
that the angle of refraction is greater than the angle of incidence.
As the latter is increased, so that the wave arrives from a
direction more nearly parallel to the boundary, we see that
the condition is reached when the direction of the refracted
wave lies along the boundary, so that no energy is actually
transmitted into the second medium. At this point the angle of
incidence is said to be the "critical angle". As the angle of
incidence is still further increased up to the limit when the
incident wave direction is practically parallel to the boundary,
there is no transmission and the whole of the incident wave
energy is reflected. This is called "total internal reflection".
The critical angle can be calculated from equation (9) by
putting $\varphi_2 = \pi/2$ radians (i.e. 90 degrees) so that

$$\sin \varphi_{\text{crit}} = c_1/c_2 \qquad \qquad \dots \quad (10)$$

where c_1 is the lower velocity.

Now the discussion above has been concerned with reflection
and refraction at a boundary between two fluid media. If one
of the media is a solid, however, the matter is much more
complicated as waves of a different type (called "shear" waves)
can be generated in the solid. But for the simple discussion
which follows, these complications may be ignored.

Since the acoustic velocity is less in air than in water, but
greater in rock, it is not possible to prevent acoustic energy
leaving the water for the air, but it is possible to avoid the
energy entering the sea-bottom by choosing a nearly horizontal
wave direction. But before this conclusion is really meaningful
we need to know *how much* of the energy is reflected and how
much transmitted at any boundary. This depends not only on

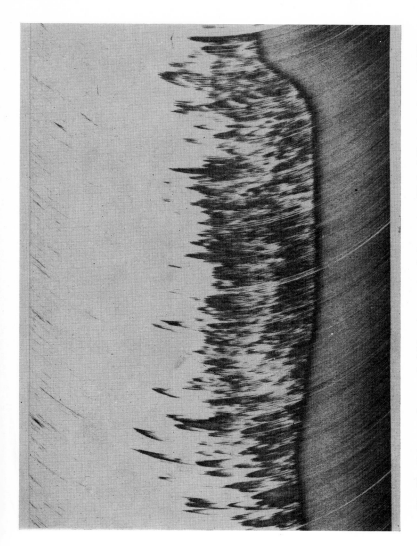

Fig. 34.—Echo-sounder record of fish, taken on chemical recorder. (Firth of Clyde, depth scale 20–50 fathoms.) (*Text page 95*)

(*Courtesy Marine Laboratories Aberdeen*)

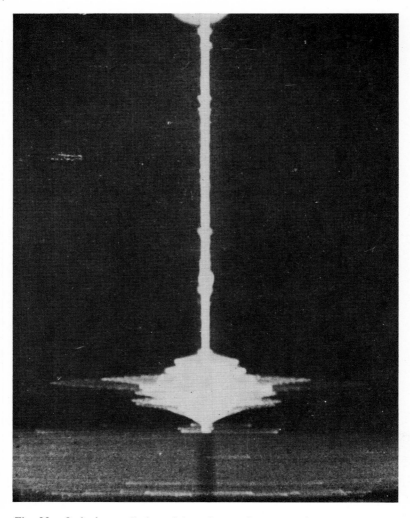

Fig. 36.—Cathode-ray display of the echo-sounder returns from the range just above the sea-bottom. The depth of water is about 30 fathoms, but the length of the trace (from top to bottom) corresponds to only 7 fathoms. Note the fish echo just above the sea-bed. (*Text page 95*)

(*Courtesy Institution of Electronic & Radio Engineers*)

Fig. 37.—Photograph of a large magnetostrictive transducer used in a whale-finding sonar equipment. The transducer is fitted with staves made up from laminations of magnetostrictive material and wound with coils of stout insulated wire. One face has a resonant frequency of 14 kc/s and the other 22 kc/s; they are separated physically by cellular rubber. (*Text page 97*) (*Courtesy Kelvin-Hughes Division of S. Smith & Sons (England) Ltd.*)

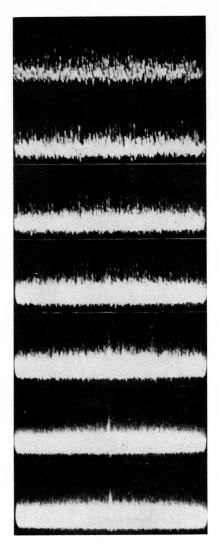

Fig. 44.—Showing the improvement in detection obtained on a rectified A-scan when the number of superposed traces is increased. The signal-to-noise ratio of the input signal is the same throughout, and the signal is a very short pulse in the middle of the trace, clearly visible in the lower photographs. In the top photograph there is only a single trace; in the succeeding photographs there are respectively 2, 5, 10, 20, 50 and 100 traces superposed. (*Text page 110*)

the relation of the velocities in the two media but also on the ratio of their densities. It is not worth going into the matter fully, since it is complicated, but the simple case when the direction of the wave is perpendicular to the surface has the simple relationship that the ratio of pressure (p_2 and p_1) of reflected and incident waves is

$$\frac{p_2}{p_1} = \frac{R_2 - R_1}{R_2 + R_1} \qquad \dots \ (11)$$

where R_1 is the acoustic resistance of the first medium and R_2 that of the second. We saw earlier that the acoustic resistance is the ratio of the acoustic pressure and the particle velocity (i.e. p/u), but it can also be expressed for a plane wave as the product of density (i.e. mass per unit volume) and acoustic velocity in the medium. Density is usually represented by ρ (the Greek letter Rho) so that acoustic resistance is given by

$$R = \rho c \qquad \dots \ (12)$$

We can now see that, for the water-air boundary, the ratio of velocities is only about 5 : 1, but the ratio of densities is about 800 : 1, and thus the acoustic resistance of water is about 4,000 times that of air. This means that the ratio p_2/p_1 as given by equation (11) is almost exactly unity. The ratio of the resistances is such that near enough all the incident energy is reflected and none transmitted when a wave reaches the water-air boundary from either side. It is practically impossible therefore for sound to enter or leave the sea through the surface. But at the bottom, the position is not so extreme. The ratio of velocities in water and rock is of the order of 1 : 3 (varying over quite a wide range) and the ratio of densities is much the same. Thus the ratio of acoustic resistances is of the order of 1 : 10, and so the reflected pressure is something like 80% of the incident pressure.* In other words, since power, which is the rate of flow of energy, is proportional to the square of the pressure in a given medium, about two-thirds of the acoustic energy is reflected and about one-third transmitted. This is,

---

* Note that when the wave originates in the medium of higher acoustic resistance, so that R_2 is less than R_1, the expression in equation (11) is negative. This merely means that the reflected wave has opposite phase to the incident wave. In the limit when R_2 is zero (or nearly so) the boundary is said to be "soft", or "pressure release", since pressure cannot be sustained in a medium of zero resistance. At the other extreme when R_2 is extremely high, the boundary is said to be "hard", since pressure is sustained but the particle velocity must be zero.

we must remember, for a direction perpendicular to the sea-bottom. This result explains why when geophysicists are trying to find out what lies beneath the sea, they are able to generate their sound-waves (usually by an explosion) in the water, knowing a useful amount of energy will be transmitted into the rocks and then out again into the water for detection. But it would be useless to have the sound source (i.e. explosion) in the air.

4.2 *Bending of beams in the sea*

Although some problems, as suggested above, arise at the boundaries, there are also refraction effects within the sea itself. This is because the acoustic velocity is not the same everywhere in the sea, but varies somewhat according to temperature, salinity and the static pressure due to depth. The main effect is usually due to temperature, since the velocity is 1,446 metres/sec at 0°C with a salinity of 35 parts per thousand, and rises by about 4·2 m/s for each 1°C rise in temperature. Halving the salinity reduces the velocity by about 20 m/s. Due to the warming effect of the sun, complicated by currents, turbulence, etc., in the water, the acoustic velocity usually varies considerably from one depth to another, but not very much horizontally.

Consider a plane wave which is travelling in a horizontal direction from our left at some vertical plane which we take as reference. The lines of equal pressure in the wave are thus straight (because it is a plane wave) and vertical. Such a line may be taken to represent the wave and is called "a wave front". It is useful in diagrams, and Fig. 30 shows a vertical wave front in the reference position on the left. Now suppose that the acoustic velocity diminishes with depth. Then a point in the upper part of the wave front will progress faster than one lower down. Thus at some time later, the wave front will not be vertical any longer, but will be sloping to the right, as indicated in the diagram. This means the direction of progression is no longer horizontal, but is sloped downwards. Clearly the effect accumulates, as shown, and the downward slope becomes greater. A receiver placed at a depth adequate to receive the wave at the reference point will clearly fail to receive appreciable energy at some point to the right. The waves have been refracted downwards.

WAVEFRONT

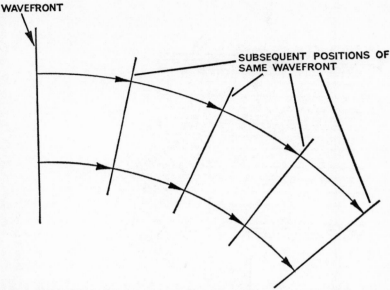

Fig. 30.—Showing bending (or refraction) of wave path when velocity is lower at greater depths.

The refracted wave will eventually reach the sea-bottom. There it will be reflected, as discussed above, and it will start to rise steeply. But the "velocity gradient", as the variation of velocity with depth is called, will bend it round again. The process goes on, and most complicated effects may arise. These are very important in sonar operation, except perhaps in vertical echo-sounding where this type of effect is not involved.

4.3 *Echoes from targets*

Returning to the reflection of acoustic waves at a boundary, we can consider the rather different case of a small object in the water which has an acoustic resistance different from that of water. The object may be a fish, submarine or other "target" (as it is usually called) which is small in relation to the distance from the acoustic source. Fig. 31 shows the situation. Waves progress from the source (transmitting transducer) and by the time they reach the target are practically plane waves. (Distances in the diagram are, of course, not realistic.) The acoustic energy intercepted by the target is largely reflected,

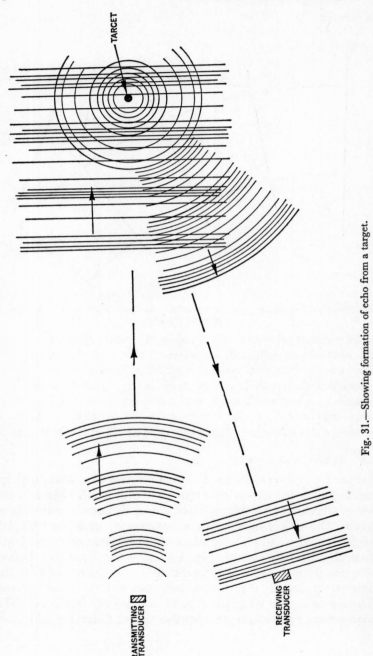

Fig. 31.—Showing formation of echo from a target.

but as the target is small, it does not send plane waves back as happened with the boundary of very large extent, but instead radiates spherical waves as shown. These travel in all directions, and may be picked up by a receiving transducer. In the diagram this is shown, for clarity, at some distance from the transmitter, but it may well be one and the same transducer when only short bursts of signal are used as for sonar. This echo-effect, as it is called, forms the basis of sonar systems.

If the target is either spherical or very small compared with the wavelength, the re-radiation of energy from it is the same in all directions. Otherwise there may be a directional effect as the target acts like an array of re-radiating sources. The "target strength" (*TS*) is a useful measure of the target, and for any given direction is expressed in decibels as

$$TS = 10 \log_{10}(I_2/I_1) \qquad \ldots \quad (13)$$

where I_1 is the acoustic intensity (power flow per unit area) of the wave incident upon the target and I_2 is that of the reflected wave at unit distance from the centre of the target. If the target is spherical, *TS* is easily calculated; let the target diameter be 2*r* units so that the acoustic power intercepted by it is $\pi r^2 I_1$. As the target is spherical, this power is re-radiated equally in all directions. At unit distance from the centre of the target, the total cross-sectional area of the radiation is 4π square units. The re-radiated intensity at unit distance is therefore $\pi r^2 I_1/4\pi$, i.e. $r^2 I_1/4$. The target strength is therefore

$$TS = 10 \log_{10}(r^2/4) \text{ decibels} \qquad \ldots \quad (14)$$

Now if *r* is 2 units, *TS* is zero decibels, so this is a standard reference size of target. The unit used in more modern work is the metre, so the reference target is a sphere of 4 metres diameter.* It is important to remember that the size of the reference depends on the unit of length used. It is desirable to avoid mixing units.

All targets smaller than the reference target have $r^2/4$ less than unity, which means that the logarithm is negative. Thus a sphere of 1 metre diameter has a target strength of -12 dB.

---

* It is perhaps confusing that the reference target is a sphere of 4 metres diameter, yet the re-radiated acoustic intensity is calculated as at 1 metre from the centre of the sphere. This is purely to preserve normal units in the work, and does not infer that intensities inside the sphere are being considered. To avoid this difficulty we could take the intensity at 10 metres from the centre, and adjust the definition of target strength accordingly; but this is obviously clumsy and inconvenient.

Sometimes a target strength is quoted as the "scattering cross-section" of the target. This is merely the cross-sectional area of a sphere which gives the same target strength as the given target in the conditions specified. Thus if σ (the Greek letter Sigma) is the scattering cross-section, the target strength is $10 \log_{10} (\sigma/4\pi)$ decibels.

Chapter 3

Basic principles of simple sonar systems

1 The equipment

Having in the previous chapter seen how acoustic waves behave, and how beams and echoes are formed, we now proceed to see how a sonar system is made to exploit them.

First it is necessary to point out that the term sonar includes all underwater acoustic systems used for detection and location (and identification where possible) of underwater objects. In Chapter 1 we mentioned the possibility of using passive or listening systems for the detection of fish noises, and it might be argued that these systems too are sonar. But we shall restrict our consideration to active systems, where an acoustic wave is sent out by the system and its echoes from the objects in the water are used as the source of information about the objects. Although in some places echo-sounders are distinguished from sonar systems as having a vertical beam while sonars have a horizontal beam, this usage is very misleading. Echo-sounders *are* sonars and work in exactly the same way. The direction of the beam does not affect the nature of the system. We shall also restrict attention to sonar systems using pulses of acoustic energy. Although continuous-wave (or almost continuous-wave) sonars can be made, their use is at present very limited and they have not found their way into fisheries operations.

1.1 *The basic scheme of a sonar system*

With the provisos set out above, we can now say that the basic scheme of a sonar system is that shown in the schematic drawing of Fig. 32 and the timing diagram of Fig. 33. These are largely self-explanatory, so discussion of them can be brief. Of course, practical systems show many variations, especially in regard to the combining of two (or more) functions in one item of equipment. Examples of this are

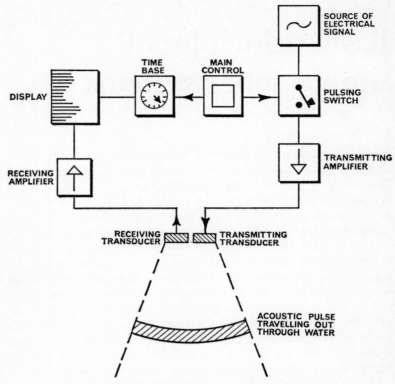

Fig. 32.—General schematic of a sonar system.

(a) the combining of the pulsing switch and the source of electrical signal, e.g. a triggered oscillatory discharge circuit;

(b) the combining of the main control and the time-base, as in the chemical recorder;

(c) the use of one transducer for both transmitting and receiving—but then a transmit/receive (or "TR") switch is needed.

Basically all systems send out from the transmitter a short burst, or pulse, of an acoustic wave at one particular frequency. This frequency is determined by the frequency of the electrical oscillation generated in the top right-hand box in Fig. 32. The duration of the pulse, as we shall see later, is very important, and is determined in the more sophisticated equipments by the pulsing switch. As this pulse travels out through the water, the time-base (which may be purely electronic as with a cathode-ray display, or mechanical as with a chemical recorder)

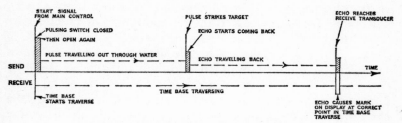

Fig. 33.—Time diagram for sonar system.

is also traversing. When the pulse of acoustic wave reaches a target, it starts being reflected as was shown in Fig. 31. It eventually reaches the receiving transducer where it is converted into an electrical signal, which is amplified and used to produce a mark on the display. The time which has elapsed between transmission and reception is exactly proportional to the distance of the target from the transducers. As the time-base has been traversing at constant speed, the point in its traverse where the echo-pulse causes a mark is at a distance from the start of the traverse also exactly proportional to the distance of the target. A simple calibration enables the distance (or "range") to be read off. Similar marks will be obtained from other targets within the beam at different ranges. Naturally, two targets which lie at slightly different angles, but within the beam, at exactly the same range cannot be distinguished.

The transmission of the pulse is repeated at regular intervals, which are determined by the need to let one pulse have time to return from the most distant range concerned before the next is sent out. For a range of half-a-mile, the repetition interval is roughly one second.

1.2 *Displays*

To the user of a sonar system, the display is the most critical part of the equipment, since it is the way in which information is presented which often determines what use can be made of it. Although most of our discussion will assume the information about echoes to be displayed visually, it is for some purposes possible and useful to present the information aurally, so that the special characteristics of the ear may be exploited. For this to be really worth while, however, the pulse must be long enough for the ear to detect any tonal qualities it may have. The incoming frequency from the transducer is changed by "heterodyning" to a lower frequency in the sensitive range of the ear, say 1,000 cycle/sec. A pulse duration of over 50 milli-seconds is required, compared with the 1 ms or so which is common in fisheries sonars. Aural detection is most useful when fast-moving targets such as whales are to be observed, since the ear can often detect the small change of pitch in the echo due to the movement of the target; this is a great help in identifica-tion and catching.

For simple sonars, the commonest type of visual display is the chemical or paper recorder, a very efficient instrument which records the received information on sensitized paper which shows a dark mark when an electric current is passed through it from the upper surface to the lower. The time-base is mechanical; the recording stylus is drawn across the paper. The paper is moved slowly in a direction at right-angles to the traverse of the stylus, so that successive traverses (which correspond to successive pulse transmissions) lie side-by-side. If the range of the target does not change, the echoes mark at the same distance in each traverse and so produce a line down the paper. If the range changes, perhaps due to the motion of the target or the ship on which the sonar is fitted, then the line is sloped relative to the paper motion.

Recorders are made in three basic types. Probably the commonest, which is frequently used in fisheries sonars, is that in which the stylus is mounted at the end of a rotating arm, so that the traverse is an arc of a circle. Switches are fitted to the driving shaft to operate the pulsing of the electrical signal at the proper instant. There may be several styluses each on a separate arm. Another type of recorder is the straight-line stylus type, in which the stylus is drawn across the paper on a straight line and then flies back rapidly. The third type is that in which a spiral conducting bar rotates on a shaft on the underside of the paper, and there is a fixed straight bar on the upper side. This is effectively a straight-line recorder but without flyback and the consequent loss of time. The straight-line recorders are naturally the best for surveying work where an accurate geographical picture may be required.

A typical recorder chart showing fish is illustrated in Fig. 34. One of the big advantages of this kind of display is the permanence of its record. This may not be especially valuable in fish catching or navigation, but it certainly is in most other applications of sonar.

Cathode-ray displays are often used—sometimes merely to supplement the recorder, and sometimes as a main display. In more complicated sonars, various kinds of "intensity-modulated" cathode-ray displays are used, such as the so-called B-scan and P.P.I., where a target is indicated by the brightening-up of the spot on the screen rather as in television, and in some ways corresponding to the marking of a target on recorder paper. But in simple sonars the cathode-ray display is generally of the "A-scan" type. This method of display was used in early radar systems before it came into use in sonar, and was then of the type shown in Fig. 35 (a), where the overall (or envelope) magnitude of the pulse was shown as a sideways deflection on the line of the time-base. This is called "rectified A-scan". Sonar displays usually use "unrectified A-scan", where the actual electrical oscillations derived from the acoustic wave vibrations are shown as a sideways deflection, as shown in Fig. 35 (b). A photograph of an actual display is shown in Fig. 36.

One big advantage which the cathode-ray display has over the recorder is that it has an electronic time-base which can move incomparably faster than the mechanical time-base. Thus although some remarkable speeds have been attained with recorders, the cathode-ray display is much more suitable when it is desired to expand just a small part of the range (e.g. just a few fathoms above the sea-bottom) to detect fish echoes clearly.

It should be noted that the signal received at the receiving transducer, for a given strength of target, decreases rapidly as the range of the target is increased due to both the spreading losses and absorption losses. For the display to be useful, therefore, the receiving amplifier needs to have an amount of amplification (or "gain") which increases with time

after a pulse is transmitted. Alternatively some form of
automatic volume control (well known to radio workers) may
be used.

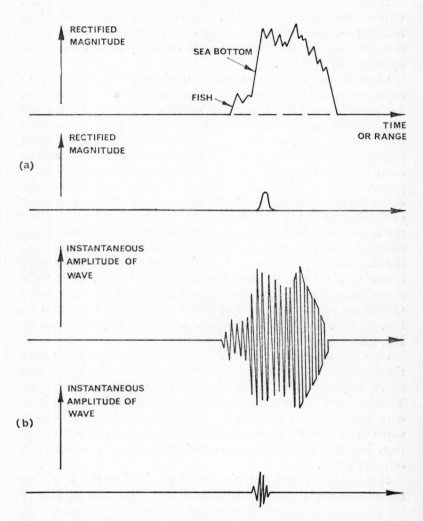

Fig. 35.—A-scan displays: (a) rectified A-scan, (b) unrectified A-scan. In each
case the upper scan shows the echoes from a large or diffuse target (e.g. the
sea-bottom with fish just above it, as observed with a vertical beam) and the lower
scan shows the echo from a single small target.

1.3 Transducers

The transducers are obviously a vital part of the system even if less obvious to the user. Their function in converting electrical oscillations into acoustic oscillations and vice versa is similar to that of the familiar loudspeaker and microphone. Indeed, it would be possible to use the same type of mechanism under water as in air, but the very different acoustic properties of water and air make the design problems very different, and much higher efficiencies of conversion can be obtained in water than in air. Whereas most loudspeakers are electro-dynamic in mechanism, i.e. they use the forces generated by the flow of current in a conductor in a magnetic field, most underwater transducers, on the other hand, use a quite different mechanism, namely that in which the dimensions of a piece of material change under the influence of a magnetic or electric field. If the field follows the electrical oscillations, then the changes in dimensions generate the acoustical oscillations and vice versa.

There are three main types of underwater electro-acoustic transducer; these are (a) magnetostrictive, (b) piezo-electric, and (c) electrostrictive.

In a magnetostrictive transducer a magnetic field is applied to a piece of suitable magnetic material, causing the dimension of the piece to decrease along the axis parallel to the field. The decrease is proportional to the strength of the field, but is still a decrease even if the field is reversed. Thus as the field, which is generated by passing the electrical oscillatory current through a coil round the material, is alternating, it is necessary to polarize the material with a steady, non-alternating field in addition if the acoustic wave is to have the same frequency as the electrical oscillation; otherwise the frequency would be doubled.

The magnetostrictive effect also operates in reverse; received acoustic signals cause compression of the material, which generates a magnetic field (or preferably varies an existing steady field) which in turn generates a voltage in the coil wound around the material. The latter is generally a fairly thick wire with tough insulation so that the whole transducer can be directly immersed in the water.

These transducers are satisfactory for frequencies up to about 100 kc/s, and are easily constructed. They are in common use still, although they are rather expensive. A typical magneto-strictive transducer used in a powerful sonar set is shown in Fig. 37.

Piezo-electric transducers use crystals in which the dimensions change according to the applied *electric* field. If the field is alternating the crystals vibrate and give an acoustic radiation; conversely if the crystals are acted on by acoustic waves then they generate an electric field. Typical piezo-electric materials used for this purpose are quartz and ammonium dihydrogen phosphate (ADP). Whereas magnetostrictive transducers typically have low impedances of only a few ohms, piezo-electric transducers have high impedances typically of the order of 10,000 ohms and this requires high voltages for only moderate acoustic powers. They also have to be fitted in a water-tight container.

Electrostrictive transducers are becoming much more widely used and seem likely to displace the other types for the majority of applications. Examples of electrostrictive materials used for transducers are barium titanate and lead zirconate-titanate, in ceramic form which can be moulded to approximately the right shape and size. The change of dimensions which produces the acoustic waves is dependent on the magnitude but not on the polarity of the applied electric field, and thus electric polarization is needed just as magnetic polarization was needed with magnetostrictive transducers. Like the others they also operate as receivers. Electrostrictive transducers generally have very convenient impedances of a few hundred ohms. They usually have to operate in a water-tight container.

Unlike loudspeakers in air, underwater transducers are naturally efficiently coupled into the water without special artifices. But they may need special mountings to permit a streamlined flow of water past them as the ship moves.

We can illustrate some ways in which piezo-electric and electrostrictive material can be assembled into a form suitable for underwater use by Figs. 38 and 39. In the form shown in Fig. 38, the element with its chosen backing is mounted in an insulating liquid, usually castor oil, and coupled into the water by means of a thin metallic diaphragm, e.g. aluminium of thickness perhaps one-thirtieth of a wavelength, or by a special rubber membrane whose acoustic resistance is the same as that of the water, so that no internal reflections occur. (Such rubber is usually called "rho-cee" rubber, after the expression ρc which is the acoustic resistance.) Alternatively the element can be bonded to a metal plate of one half-wavelength in thickness, but although this gives a better mechanical design, the transducer gives an effective response over a narrower band of frequencies.

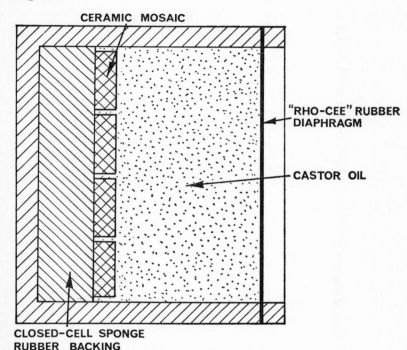

Fig. 38.—Diametric cross-section of an oil-immersion transducer.

At low frequencies, quarter or half-wave crystal or ceramic elements become very thick and so are difficult to manufacture and require large driving voltages. It is then best to make up a transducer from a slice (or slices) of material made up in sandwich form between blocks of metal, as shown in Fig. 39.

Although there is a good deal of science in the design of transducers, there is also a very large proportion of art. This makes it difficult—and unnecessary—to go very fully into the subject here.

2   Theoretical considerations of sonar systems

In the previous descriptive account of sonar systems there was a conspicuous absence of quantitative information. Nothing was said about what frequency and pulse-duration should be used, nothing about beam widths, amount of amplification, etc. But now we see what sonar systems are like we can discuss some of these theoretical matters. It seems simplest to start with the problem of pulse-duration and the consequent frequency-bandwidth needs of the system.

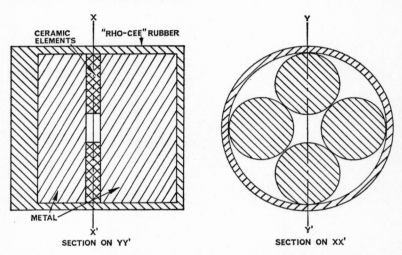

Fig. 39.—Ceramic sandwich transducer as used for small echo-sounders.

2.1   *Pulse duration, bandwidth and range resolution*

The duration of each pulse transmitted in a sonar system is, in its simplest conception, merely the time which elapses between the switching-on of the pulsing switch in Fig. 32 and its switching-off. Let this time be T seconds.

Now this pulse has the voltage/time waveform shown at (a) in Fig. 40 (although there would generally be more cycles of the wave within it than it has been convenient to draw.) It has to pass through the transmitting transducer, the water and the receiving transducer and amplifier before finally being displayed as an echo. We will assume the target is a very small sphere so that it does nothing to distort the pulse-wave;

it merely reflects it. Moreover, we can assume within the limits of the present discussion that the water is a perfect acoustic-transmission medium; its properties hardly affect the pulse-duration and bandwidth problem. Thus we have to consider just the effect on the pulse of the transducers and amplifier(s).

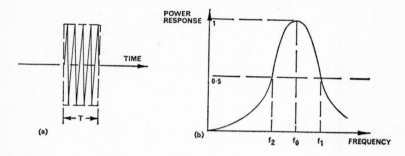

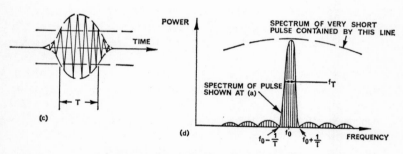

Fig. 40.—Illustrating pulses and bandwidths.

These units, which we may refer to collectively as the "circuit", do not pass waves or oscillations of all frequencies equally well. Indeed, the range of frequencies over which they are effective is usually very restricted, and a graph of the variation of power response with frequency is typically as shown at (b) in Fig. 40. There is generally a central frequency (f_0) at which the response is greatest; if f_1 and f_2 are the upper and lower frequencies at which the power response is one-half of the maximum, then $f_1 - f_2$ is called the "half-power bandwidth" or "3-dB bandwidth", or usually just "the bandwidth".

Let us suppose that the frequency of the electrical oscillation within the pulse is chosen to coincide with the greatest response of the circuit, i.e. it is f_0. But it is a fundamental property of waves and oscillations that they can consist of one single frequency only so long as they persist for ever, i.e. have no start or finish. In practice this means that they must go on for a relatively long time. So for practical purposes we may regard the source of oscillation as having a single frequency. The switching on and off involved in generating a pulse, however, causes other frequencies to be generated besides the frequency f_0. Let the interval between repetitions of the pulse be T_p sec. Then frequencies are generated at intervals of $1/T_p$ cycles/sec to each side of f_0 with relative power levels as shown in the diagram of (d) in Fig. 40. Evidently the bulk of the power is spread over only the central part of this "spectrum", and we can say, in rough terms, that the pulse has a bandwidth given by the half-power bandwidth f_T which is (in an accurately drawn diagram) very close to $1/T$ cycles/sec.

The pulse spectrum we have been referring to has clearly a bandwidth less than that of the circuit (as at (b) in Fig. 40) and so the pulse will pass through the circuit quite readily and with very little distortion of the "square" envelope shape.

Now suppose that the pulse is very greatly reduced in duration, so that the spectrum is very much widened, as shown by the dashed containing line in (d) of Fig. 40. Then when this pulse passes through the circuit, most of its power is stopped by the circuit and only those frequency components within the bandwidth of the circuit can pass. This means that the envelope shape of the pulse coming out of the receiver is very unlike the square shape of the transmitted pulse. It will be rounded and greatly elongated; working backwards from the previous arguments we see that it will have an effective duration of about $1/(f_1-f_2)$ seconds.

A practical limit is reached when the bandwidth of the circuit and the duration of the pulse are roughly matched, i.e. when $f_1-f_2 = 1/T$. Then the received pulse looks as shown at (c) in Fig. 40. It still has about the same duration as the transmitted pulse if the duration is measured at the half-amplitude levels as shown; and its maximum amplitude is only a few per cent below what it would be if the circuit bandwidth had not restricted it.

Another way of looking at this matter of pulse distortion is to realize that all circuits and mechanical devices (e.g. a transducer) which have elements like capacitance and mass, which store energy, cannot respond to any stimulus instantly. They have inertia. So they cannot possibly pass a square pulse without distortion; they require time for the response to build up, and then time for it to die away again. If the pulse is much shorter than the response time, then effectively the pulse is not passed on.

So we see that pulse duration and bandwidth are inseparably related. But why are the actual values important?

Bandwidth, by itself, is important for two reasons. One is that the wider the band the more noise is let through to spoil detection of the echoes; we shall discuss the effect of noise again later. The other is that, as we have just said, all mechanical devices have elements like mass and springiness which store energy or oscillate; transducers inevitably use pieces of material which have preferred frequencies of vibration. (Think of a tuning fork for a familiar example of preferred frequency of vibration, or "resonance" as it is called.) The limited bandwidth of the circuit as shown at (b) in Fig. 40 is due to this effect. It is indeed difficult to make transducers with a bandwidth wider than about one-fifth of f_0 (which is what is meant when it is said that a transducer has a Q-factor of about 5). So if we ask for a shorter pulse duration we may be asking the designer for a transducer which may be very difficult (and therefore expensive)—or even impossible—to design and make. It should be noted that the bandwidth over two transducers is somewhat less than for one alone. The amplifiers need not inherently restrict the bandwidth, but usually do so.

Pulse duration is fundamentally important because it determines the minimum separation in range of two small targets which need to be detected as separate targets. If the outgoing pulse encounters a small target at a particular range R_1 then a sudden small burst of the transmitted frequency is returned to the receiver. If the transducers and amplifiers have a very wide bandwidth, the pulse envelope shape remains square all through and of the correct duration T. If, in addition

to the target at range R_1 there is another small target at a very
slightly greater range R_2, then this too will give a correct echo
pulse, and the two objects will appear separately at the display,
with a recognisable gap between them, if R_2—R_1 is greater than
L, where L is the length of the pulse in the water. Evidently
$L = cT$. The targets are said to be resolved. If R_2—R_1 is less
than L, the two targets do not appear with sufficient separation
to be distinguished; they are not resolved.

Obviously, as inadequate bandwidth in the circuit causes
the pulse to be distorted and lengthened, it spoils the resolution
even if the pulse duration were originally short enough.

Typical numerical values are $T = 0 \cdot 001$ sec (or 1 millisecond) and bandwidth just over 1,000 cycles/sec, giving
$L = 1 \cdot 5$ metres or nearly 5 feet.

2.2 *Noise*

In the foregoing discussion we have assumed that the pulse
wave is the only excitation that the receiver is subject to. In
practice this is not a realistic assumption. There are two other
important sources of excitation

(a) noise, and
(b) reverberation.

We shall now consider the effects of noise.

By noise we mean any power produced at the output of the
receiver which is not due to our own transmissions. One
possible source of noise is, of course, the transmissions of other
sonar systems operating in the vicinity; but these are very
easily recognized and rarely prove a serious problem. What is
more serious, because unavoidable, is the general background
of acoustic noise in the water and the electrical noise background in the receiver. The sources are

(a) "thermal" noise in the water due to the random motions
of molecules,

(b) "thermal" noise in the input resistance of the receiver,
and "shot" and "flicker" noise in the amplifier, all due to the
random motions of electrons,

(c) "sea-state" noise due to waves breaking and other
disturbances in the sea,

(d) animal and man-made noises, e.g. propeller noise, harbour noise, etc.

(e) electrical interference from other equipment on the ship, radio signals, etc.

Clearly we can make no simple allowance for (d), and we shall not discuss it further; but acoustically-transmitted noise from one's own ship is often important. Good electrical design should reduce (e) to negligible proportions.

Noise of the types (a), (b) and (c) are characterized by having a waveform which is of random nature, i.e. is not regular, successive peaks being of different and unpredictable heights and spacings. In consequence the power of the noise is spread continuously and smoothly over a wide band of frequency. But since the receiving transducer and amplifier restrict the band of frequencies which can be received, the noise at the output of the receiver is "band-limited" and the rate at which its amplitude can vary (even though random) is restricted by the bandwidth in the same way as the pulse build-up and decay is limited. The waveform of the noise, therefore, is of the general kind shown at (b) in Fig. 41.

Since noise has no steady amplitude, it cannot be measured as simply as a sinusoidal signal. It is usually measured as a mean power level, averaged over a reasonable period of time —many times the reciprocal of the bandwidth. In the electrical circuit it is often convenient to refer to the r.m.s. (i.e. root-mean-square) voltage of the noise; this is the square-root of the mean power multiplied by the resistance of the circuit, i.e. $\sqrt{(PR)}$.

Noise of types (a) and (b)—the thermal noise—has the same power level in all frequency bands of the same width irrespective of where they occur in the actual frequency range, but is dependent on the transducer and amplifier resistance values and on their temperatures. Noise of type (c)—the sea-state noise—is different in that its power level per unit bandwidth falls as the frequency is raised, and is also dependent on the state of the sea. The fall of the power level with frequency is, for all sea-states, almost proportional to the square of the reciprocal of the frequency, i.e. noise power is proportional to $1/f^2$. To fix the order of magnitude of this noise we can take the noise intensity for sea-state 4 to be about 130 dB below 1 watt per square metre per 1 cycle/sec of bandwidth at 10 kc/s. Thus in sonar systems operating at low frequencies the dominant factor is sea-state noise, but at high

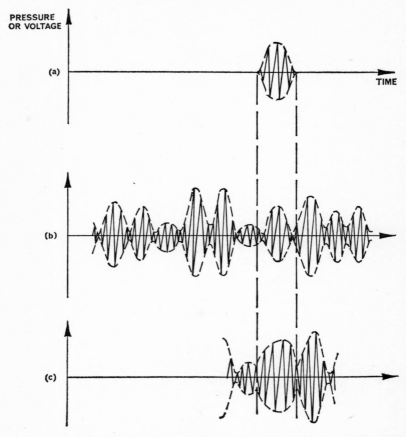

Fig. 41.—Showing effect of noise on pulse: (a) pulse alone, (b) noise alone, (c) pulse-plus-noise.

frequencies it is thermal noise. The changeover frequency depends, of course, on the sea-state, but is in the region of 100 kc/s.

The effect of noise on the detection of the echo pulse depends naturally on the ratio of the pulse power (or pressure or voltage) to that of the noise, i.e. on the signal-to-noise ratio. This is sometimes expressed as a power ratio and sometimes as a voltage ratio, but when expressed in decibels instead of a plain ratio there is no difference, since the signal-to-noise ratio (SNR) is then either $10 \log_{10} (P_{\text{signal}}/P_{\text{noise}})$ or $20 \log_{10} (V_{\text{signal}}/V_{\text{noise}})$ which are the same, since $(P_{\text{signal}}/P_{\text{noise}}) = (V_{\text{signal}}/V_{\text{noise}})^2$.

For a SNR around unity (or zero decibels) the situation is roughly as shown in Fig. 41. At (a) we have the pulse alone, rounded in envelope shape by passing through the transducers and amplifiers. At (b) we have some random noise as passed by the receiver. When the pulse is received it is added to the noise as shown at (c). The way in which the waveforms add depends on the phase relationship at each instant, and as the phase of the noise is also random, the resultant envelope shape is not just the sum of the pulse and noise envelopes. Clearly the detection of the echo-pulse is now a matter of some doubt; with the phases as drawn it would hardly be detected, but with more favourable phases it might be. For SNR = 1 (i.e. zero decibels) the probability of detecting the pulse is, in fact, very near to 50% and the probability of making a false detection through mistaking a large noise peak for a signal pulse is also about 50%. This condition where the probabilities are 50% is often called the threshold of detection.

In practice, it is the envelope of the resultant waveform which we examine for the pulse, whether it is displayed as an A-scan as in Fig. 41 or by intensity of marking as in the chemical recorder. This means that the combined noise and signal is effectively rectified*—whether by an electrical rectifier or by a visual process is immaterial—and the process involves some interaction between signal and noise. That this must be so becomes clear when we realize that the envelope of the resultant of signal-plus-noise is not just a plain addition of the individual envelopes (as previously explained in connection with Fig. 41) so that the envelope is a complex interaction of the signal and noise in which there are new components which involve the signal but which are no longer identifiable as signal; these add effectively to the noise. Thus, in qualitative terms, we see that the signal-to-noise ratio must be worsened

* This matter is discussed more fully in Appendix III.

by the envelope-taking process. But we must consider what is meant by SNR in the envelope.

In detecting the pulse in the resultant envelope we look for a rise in level over the mean level of the whole envelope, and can detect it if it is large enough compared with the noise fluctuations. It is almost invariably the voltage which is displayed, not the power, so the envelope SNR is reasonably defined as the change in mean voltage level due to the addition of the signal, relative to the r.m.s. value of the fluctuations of the noise about the mean when no signal is present. In taking a mean voltage, a factor of $\sqrt{2}$ comes in, so that when the input SNR is good, and the interaction effects are negligible, the envelope (or output) SNR is equal to $\sqrt{2}$ times the input SNR expressed as a voltage (not a power) ratio. But when the input SNR is poor (say below zero dB), the interaction effects cause the output SNR to be worse than the input by almost the amount of the input SNR. As an example, when the input SNR is −20 dB (i.e. the signal-to-noise voltage ratio is 0·1) the output SNR is about −39 dB (or a voltage ratio of 0·0105). Fig. 42 shows the relationship graphically over a wide range of SNR.

We are now in a position to see more clearly the significance of the bandwidth in relation to noise which was briefly mentioned in the previous section of this chapter. If the bandwidth were allowed to be say ten times that really necessary to pass the pulse, the input noise power would be ten times (or 10 dB) higher, and if the SNR were marginal to start with, this would reduce the output SNR by nearly 20 dB. It is clearly necessary to keep the system bandwidth (especially at the receiving side) as low as the pulse permits.*

It is possible that in spite of keeping the bandwidth to a minimum the output SNR is not good enough to permit detection of the object of interest. Then matters can be improved, of course, by increasing the transmitted pulse power. But another way of improving detection is to use several successive pulses in the same position. What happens then is that, since the noise is random, the noise peaks come

---

* A slight increase in bandwidth may be necessary to allow for the so-called Doppler shift in frequency when the target is moving toward or away from the transducers. In short-pulse systems as used for fish detection this is negligible, but in long-pulse systems detecting fast objects, it may be appreciable.

in a different place in each trace on the recorder (say), but the echo pulse comes in the same place each time. If the traces are superposed, or set out side-by-side as in the chemical recorder, the echo gradually becomes more detectable as the number of traces is increased. It is found that perhaps ten traces will make detection near enough certain although the input SNR

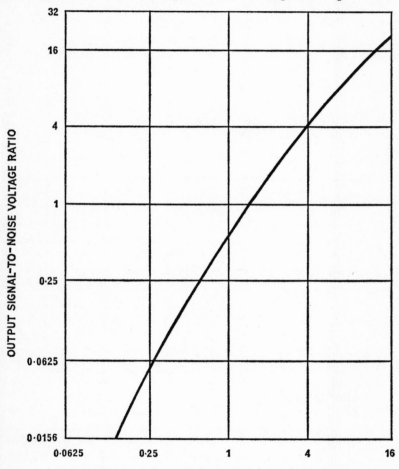

Fig. 42.—Showing the effect of taking the wave envelope (or rectification) on signal-to-noise ratio.

is only unity and detection on one trace is a very uncertain 50%. Thereafter nearly certain detection is obtainable at ever-worsening SNR's as the number of traces is increased, as shown from experimental results in Fig. 43. The word

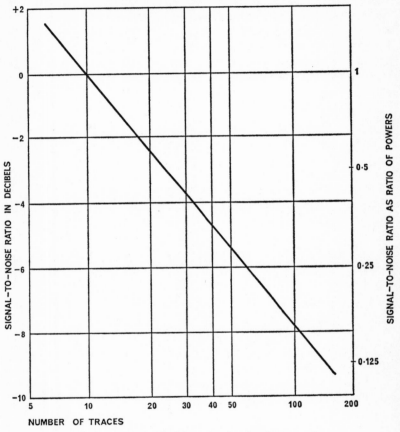

Fig. 43.—Threshold of detection in chemical recorder.

"threshold" of detection is here used to denote the lowest SNR at which detection is almost completely certain (say better than 95%). Fig. 44 shows photographs of rectified A-scan displays of a single pulse return and of several super-posed returns. While the echo signal is not detectable in the first, it is clearly detectable when the number of superposed traces is large enough. We may conclude that repeated observation (where practicable) is an effective means of combating noise.

It is clear that since the mean noise level does not vary with time, it is just a background which becomes significant as the returning echo pulses diminish in power as the range from which they come increases. Noise therefore forms a potential limitation to the maximum range of detection of the sonar system. Often, however, a more serious limitation is reverberation, which we shall now proceed to consider.

2.3 *Reverberation*

In the previous section, noise was defined as any power produced in the output of the receiver which does not originate with our own acoustic transmissions. We now have to consider the unwanted output of the receiver which is due to our own transmissions, namely the reverberation background.

Reverberation is the scattering back of the transmitted pulse to the transducers by all the particles and irregularities in the water, on its surface, and on the bottom, which cannot be regarded as targets. Since, in general, these scatterers are distributed widely in angle and range, the reverberation forms a background at all times after the transmission of a pulse, although its level falls with time, since later reverberation returns necessarily come from a greater distance. Thus reverberation is different from noise in two main respects:

(a) its level is, in general, higher at the time echoes are being received from short ranges than at later times after a pulse transmission when any echoes received come from longer ranges,

(b) since it is produced by our own transmission, its power level is directly proportional to the energy in the transmitted pulse.

Reverberation is similar to noise in that its waveform is random since the particles, etc., from which it is scattered are distributed at random, and generally moving relative to the beam; and the detection of an echo-pulse against it is dependent on the same factors. But since reverberation is the scattering of the transmitted pulse, its frequency spectrum is more or less the same as that of the pulse, and consequently the ratio of echo-pulse level to reverberation level (the signal-to-reverberation ratio or SRR) is not very sensitive to the bandwidth of the receiver.

The main consequences of the differences listed above, (a) and (b), are that

(i) reverberation is a potential obstacle to the detection of the echo at all ranges,

(ii) the energy in the echo and the energy in the reverberation are both proportional to that in the transmitted pulse and, therefore, are proportional to one another. Thus if the detection of the echo were determined by its *energy* level relative to that of the reverberation, detection could not be improved by raising the transmitted energy.

Since so many sonars work under reverberation-limited conditions, rather than noise-limited conditions, these two points lead to a common general philosophy that there is often not much advantage in using high acoustic power levels in sonar.

However, it should be observed that detection of the echo from a small target (as distinct from a large diffuse one) is more usually dependent, not on its energy, but on its pressure (and hence voltage) *amplitude*. This can be seen most clearly in the A-scan display, but it applies to almost all displays. Increasing the amplitude of the transmitted pulse will, of course, merely increase the amplitude of the reverberation and the echo in the same proportion and so will not improve detection. But if instead the pulse duration is reduced (and the bandwidth therefore increased), the transmitted energy is reduced since energy equals power times duration, power being proportional to the square of amplitude. This reduction in energy reduces the reverberation level. It also reduces the echo energy, but it does not reduce the echo amplitude since the transmitted amplitude is unchanged. Thus detection is improved. Because of this feature, SRR is best defined in terms of the ratio of echo amplitude to the r.m.s. amplitude of the reverberation.

Thus in reverberation-limited conditions the pulse duration should be as short as possible. This is also an advantage in that it improves the range resolution of the sonar. But a limit is ultimately reached, because a progressive reduction in pulse duration means a progressive increase in bandwidth and a progressively-increased noise level; thus eventually the system becomes noise-limited and its effective range of detection is reduced. The practical difficulty of obtaining transducers with a wide enough bandwidth may, of course, set a limit before noise-limitation is reached.

We have said that reverberation is a potential obstacle to detection at all ranges. But it is a greater potential obstacle at greater ranges. This is easily seen: as the range increases, the width of the acoustic beam (in feet or metres, not in degrees) increases too. Thus a target of given size forms a smaller proportion of the beam width as the range increases. But, in general, the reverberation comes from the whole or at any rate a large proportion of the beam width; therefore the SRR worsens as range increases. The situation in a typical case is shown in Fig. 45.

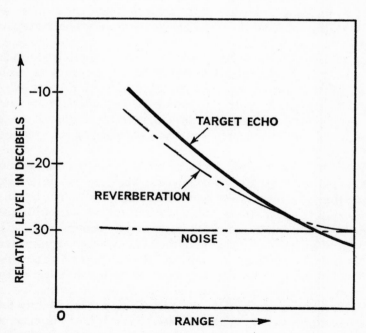

Fig. 45.—Typical relationship between target echo and reverberation and noise.

We must now turn to an examination of the different kinds of reverberation and their orders of magnitude and importance. If the sonar is operating with its beam clear of the surface and the bottom—as an echo-sounder does in the ranges less than the depth of water, or as a sonar with slightly tilted, almost horizontal, beam does in deep water—then the whole of the reverberation energy is the result of scattering of the transmitted pulse by small organisms, bubbles, turbulent regions and any other inhomogeneities in the volume of the water, so it is called "volume reverberation". As may be imagined, the general level of this reverberation varies greatly from place to place and time to time. To study it we need to use a measure which is characteristic of the sea but not of the sonar (except for any variation with frequency). We can define a reverberation strength (or scattering strength) analogous to target strength. The volume-reverberation strength is the ratio (in decibels) of the reverberation intensity (I_2) at unit distance from the centre of a sphere containing unit volume of the sea, to the incident intensity (I_1). Thus it may be written as $10 \log_{10}(I_2/I_1)$. The unit of distance is usually one metre or one yard.

It is found that the volume-reverberation strength is typically of the order of -80 to -100 dB. This is low compared with most target strengths, and so volume reverberation is not often a serious limitation. Even the deep-scattering layer of relatively dense plankton (referred to in Chapter 1), regarded as a source of volume reverberation, has a strength of only around -60 to -70 dB.

When the sonar beam includes some of the sea-bottom, as illustrated in Fig. 46, "bottom reverberation" is produced when the pulse reaches the bottom. Since the bottom is usually quite rough, with stones, etc., comparable in size with the wavelength, the amount of acoustic energy scattered back is relatively large. In that region of the beam where a transmitted pulse has not reached the bottom at any part of the cross-section of the beam, detection of a target is not affected by bottom reverberation. But in the rest of the beam, shaded in Fig. 46, a target can be detected only if it is not masked by the bottom reverberation. It can be seen that this is of importance in any sonar intended for use in demersal fishing, since of those fish which are at a sufficiently small distance from the bottom to be caught in a trawl and are in the sonar beam at any instant, most are in the shaded area.

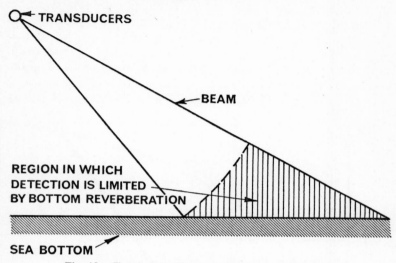

Fig. 46.—Showing significance of bottom reverberation.

The properties of the bottom in relation to reverberation can be described by the bottom-reverberation strength defined as the ratio in decibels of the reverberation intensity (I_2) at unit distance from unit area of the bottom, to the incident intensity (I_1), i.e. once again as $10 \log_{10}(I_2/I_1)$. But in this case, the reverberation intensity is found to depend very considerably on the angle which the line joining the unit area of bottom to the transducer makes relative to the bottom. This is called the "grazing angle". The reverberation strength is much greater when this line is nearly perpendicular to the bottom than when it is almost parallel to the bottom. Thus a sonar which attempts to get a long range in shallow water is helped by this feature. The reverberation strength also depends very greatly on the smoothness or roughness of the bottom. Some typical experimental measurements are shown in very much smoothed-out form in Fig. 47. Bottom reverberation depends to some extent on the frequency, since a shingle, for example, which behaves as a smooth surface to a low-frequency wave with a long wavelength will behave as a rough surface to a high-frequency wave. But there is very little evidence that the dependence of reverberation strength on frequency is at all significant. It can be seen that bottom reverberation is potentially much more serious than volume reverberation—to the extent of 60 dB or so, depending on pulse duration and beam position, etc.—which is a million-to-one in power ratio.

If the sonar beam includes some of the wavy surface of the sea, reverberation is produced by the surface in much the same way as the bottom. The surface reverberation strength is usually

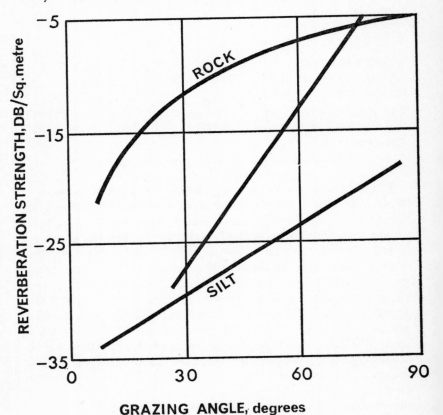

Fig. 47.—Typical values of reverberation strength of sea-bottom at various grazing angles. The middle graph shows that steeper dependence on grazing angle is sometimes found.

intermediate between bottom and volume reverberation strength, and is equally variable.

The calculation of *total* reverberation strength, i.e. the effective target strength which gives the total reverberation return at a given instant of time after the transmission of the pulse, is simple enough in the case of volume reverberation, as illustrated at (a) in Fig. 48. The return comes from the whole cross-section of the beam, and at the given instant is the summation of the reverberation from the range reached by the leading edge of the pulse at the time which enables the scattered wave from it to be received back at that instant, right through the intermediate ranges to that shorter range reached by the trailing edge of the pulse at a later time which enables the scattered wave still to be received back at the same instant. The interval of range from which the reverberation is collected is thus one-half of the pulse length, i.e. $\frac{1}{2}L(=\frac{1}{2}cT)$. The total reverberation strength at this particular time is therefore $\frac{1}{2}L$ *times* the cross-sectional area of the beam *times* the unit reverberation strength.

For bottom reverberation (and correspondingly for surface reverberation where relevant) the situation is rather different, as shown at (b) in Fig. 48. Here a slanting beam (the axis of which makes an angle β to the bottom) intercepts the bottom between ranges d_1 and d_2. Until the pulse reaches d_1 there is no bottom reverberation. After that, the reverberation level builds up, and at any instant is the summation of returns from an interval of range equal to half the pulse length, as with volume reverberation. But the area of bottom from which the return comes is approximately the transverse width of the beam times $\frac{1}{2}L/\cos \beta$ if $\frac{1}{2}L$ is less than $d_2 - d_1$; otherwise it is the area of cross-section of the beam divided by $\cos \beta$. (Note, $\cos \beta$ is never greater than unity, so the effective area is increased by being divided by $\cos \beta$—but usually not sufficiently to cancel out the steep dependence on grazing angle shown in Fig. 47.) The total reverberation strength at the particular instant is therefore this area multiplied by the unit reverberation strength as given for the grazing angle β (see Fig. 47).

If the beam is nearly horizontal, as it usually is in shallow water, then β is nearly zero, and the reverberation area is just half the pulse length times the transverse width of the beam.

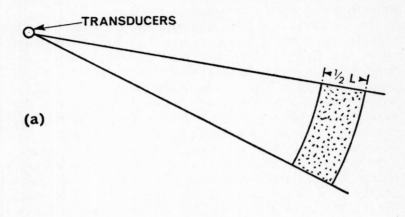

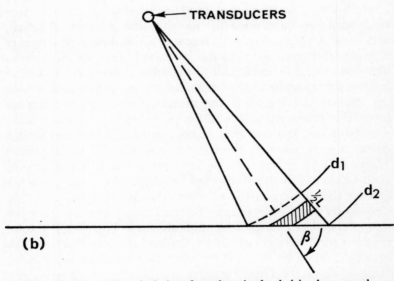

Fig. 48.—To illustrate the calculation of reverberation level: (a) volume reverberation, (b) bottom reverberation.

In this case, too, bottom reverberation is received from quite short ranges onwards, and almost the whole of the working range is subject to bottom reverberation.

Although it is not easy to generalize about when a sonar system may be expected to be reverberation-limited (i.e. its limit of detection is dictated by reverberation and not by noise) and when noise-limited, it is fairly safe to say that a system operating in fairly shallow water with reasonable power (say greater than 100 watts acoustic power) and with not too narrow a beam (say at least a few degrees) or too short a pulse (say at least 1 millisecond) will be reverberation-limited, especially if the bottom is stony or rough. On the other hand, sonar operation in deep water is more likely to be noise-limited. But, in design, detailed calculations must be made for the specific conditions of each case.

2.4 *The sonar equation*

The actual determination of the main design parameters of a sonar system, that is to say, of those quantities, dimensions, frequencies, pulse duration, etc., on which the performance depends, is clearly a very complicated problem since there are so many variables. But the various considerations which we have described in this and the previous chapters are to some extent summarized in what is known as the "sonar equation". This can perhaps most conveniently be expressed in this form, where all quantities are in decibels:

$$2N = I_S - I_N + TS - D \qquad \qquad \dots \quad (1)$$

where N = maximum permissible propagation loss between transducer and target (one way only)

I_S = intensity of pulse wave at unit distance from the transmitting transducer

I_N = intensity of noise, or reverberation from the maximum distance (d) of target, referred to the receiving transducer

TS = target strength

D = recognition differential

Each of these terms, except TS which has already been adequately defined, needs some further explanation.

The propagation loss between transducer and target comprises two main components, which we have already discussed, namely the spreading loss and the absorption loss. In a medium without boundaries the former follows the inverse square law, and the latter was given in Fig. 23 as so many decibels— say a dB—per unit distance. In the sea, with its boundaries at surface and bottom, there is usually some departure from the inverse-square spreading, and we can write H for this discrepancy, or transmission anomaly, in decibels. Thus, if d is the range, or distance of target from transducer,

$$N = 20 \log_{10} d + ad + H \text{ decibels} \qquad \text{... (2)}$$

If the transmitting transducer transmits W watts of acoustic pulse power into the water, then if it were omni-directional (i.e. produced no beam) the intensity at unit distance would be $W/4\pi$, since the cross-sectional area of the acoustic path at unit distance is 4π. But if it has a beam, produced as previously discussed, then the intensity (I_S) along the centre of the beam will be much greater, since the power is concentrated into the beam. The ratio of this intensity to $W/4\pi$ is called the "directivity factor", and ten times the logarithm of this is called the "directivity index", DI, in decibels. Thus

$$I_S = 10 \log_{10} W + DI - 10 \log_{10}(4\pi) \text{ decibels}$$
$$= 10 \log_{10} W + DI - 11 \text{ decibels} \qquad \text{... (3)}$$
$$\text{(relative to 1 watt per unit area)}$$

If the sonar is noise-limited, I_N is the intensity of noise referred to the receiving transducer, measured in decibels relative to 1 watt per unit area. Generally the noise in the sea arises more or less equally in all directions, and measurements of noise are made with omni-directional transducers, and quoted as "isotropic" noise levels. If the noise arising in the receiver itself is negligible in comparison (as is usually the case below 100 kc/s or so), then I_N is equal to the omni-directional or isotropic noise level (in decibels) reduced by the directivity index of the receiving transducer, which we assume to be the same DI as for the transmitting transducer.

If the sonar is reverberation-limited, I_N may be inserted as the reverberation level at the receiver; but it is probably easier to work out the SRR (echo signal-to-reverberation ratio) knowing the target strength TS, the reverberation strength and the cross-section of the beam, or to obtain a graph like that of Fig. 45. If this is satisfactory, i.e. SRR is greater than D (see below) at all ranges of importance, then the sonar equation is used, with I_N as the *noise* intensity, for determining the transmitted power required.

The recognition differential, D, is the SNR or SRR required to permit reliable detection and/or recognition of the target. In view of the improvement of detection threshold produced by the use of a number of successive pulse transmissions displayed together, as discussed in connection with Fig. 43, the specifying of D requires a prior specification of how many pulses may be directed in one direction before the sonar beam is moved on to a different direction. Thus D may vary from, say, +6 dB (for one pulse) to −6 dB or lower (if many pulses will be available).

Since equation (1) and its subsidiaries (2) and (3) relate all the factors involved in the specification of the sonar performance they can be used as the basis for design. For instance, if everything else is specified, the power W can be calculated; or if everything else is specified, the size of target which may be detected can be calculated. But there are always a lot of "ifs" and "buts" in sonar work. It is hard to put a value to H, the transmission anomaly; for instance, refraction due to thermal effects in the sea (see Chapter 2) may vary it enormously. Even TS is not always known at all well, as with fish, the acoustic properties of which are still the subject of much investigation. But in spite of these difficulties, the sonar equation must make a starting point in all design work. It may be, furthermore, that it is necessary to decide what frequency to use for the sonar, and this can be determined indirectly from the sonar equation since a in equation (2) is a function of frequency—see Fig. 23—and so is DI if a fixed size of transducer is specified, since the beamwidth depends on the dimensions in wavelengths and not in metres or inches.

A final word should be said on the application of all this to vertical-beam sonars or echo-sounders. For navigational purposes, when the objective is to record the echo from the sea-bottom, the value of TS is the total reverberation strength for perpendicular incidence, i.e. grazing angle of 90 degrees. Unless the volume reverberation is very exceptionally high and the target strength of the bottom very exceptionally low, detection of the bottom will be limited by noise. For the detection of fish and small objects on or near the bottom, but whose echoes are not obscured by the bottom echo, the limitation may be volume reverberation or noise—but most likely the latter.

Chapter 4

Some typical sonar designs

1 General

So far we have been concerned mainly with the principles underlying sonar systems, and it is desirable to complete the picture with a brief description of some typical sonar equipments which are available on the commercial market, together with a typical calculation of expected performance. This is not, of course, the place to give details of construction and appearance, as these are very easily obtained from the manufacturers' sales pamphlets.

If we look at the range of sonar equipments available on the British market, we find it embraces the following types of equipment:

(a) Very simple echo-sounders intended solely as navigational instruments for smaller boats operating in coastal waters; the only requirement is to indicate the depth of the sea-bottom, and this may be done by very simple indicators such as a ring of neon lamps, one of which is flashed by the echo, or a simple pointer instrument. Such an equipment is often battery operated, and works with very low acoustic power.

(b) Simple and transportable echo-sounders intended for navigational and fish-finding purposes on the smaller fishing boats; chemical recorders with paper chart are used. The total power supply required is probably less than 100 watts, the frequency of the acoustic signal is about 50 kc/s, the beam-width about 45 degrees, and the bottom can be recorded, in good conditions, up to perhaps 500–600 metres (say 300 fathoms).

(c) Higher-power echo-sounders mainly for navigational purposes; chemical recorders with paper chart are used. The total power supply required may be 200–300 watts, and the acoustic power of the signal pulse (which, of course, has a duration of only perhaps one-thousandth of the repetition period and so may have an instantaneous power in excess of the total power drawn into the equipment) may be as much as 300–400 watts. The signal frequency may be 30–50 kc/s, and the maximum depth recordable might exceed 2,000 metres or 1,000 fathoms. The recorder scale would embrace only a portion of the total depth, the zero being offset by various amounts, as desired, so that an enlarged presentation of the bottom profile is obtained. For work in shallow water, a faster stylus traverse is used, selected by a knob control. By using separate transmit and receive transducers and so obviating the need for a changeover switch, and by using a short enough pulse, depths as low as 0·6 metre (or 2 feet) may be measured.

(d) High-power echo-sounders with many refinements for fish-finding purposes. The total power consumption is about 2·5 kilowatts, the acoustic power of the signal pulse may be as high as 4 kilowatts with adjustable pulse duration from 0·5 to 2 milliseconds, and a signal frequency of 30 kc/s. Three different displays are provided: a normal chemical recorder with adjustable ranges up to 900 metres or 480 fathoms, a very fast sweep chemical recorder with a total range of 8 metres to give a scale expansion at any desired position in the range (e.g. the region just above the sea-bottom where bottom trawls are effective), and a cathode-ray display to give an enlarged picture of the echoes from fish as shown in Fig. 35. "Sea-bed lock" and "white-line" recording are available. The former means that instead of the depth of an echo fluctuating as the ship pitches and tosses, its position is stabilized with respect to the sea-bed; this is done, for example, by storing the information regarding the depth of the sea-bed from the previous pulse and using it to set the zero reference for the next trace on the recorder. The "white-line" principle is that the electronic equipment distinguishes between the small echoes from fish and the powerful echo from the bottom, and suppresses the latter for a very short interval of time after receipt, so, in effect, drawing a white line along the bottom profile. Thus any fish immediately above the bottom show up clearly as fish (and not as bottom) by lying above the white line. The beamwidth is about 10 degrees fore and aft and 15 degrees transversely.

(e) Fish-finding sonar equipments with beams in a near-horizontal position as well as vertical; the former beam is "trainable", i.e. it may be swung round from the port quarter to the ahead position and on to the starboard quarter, a total swing of 270 degrees. With a beamwidth of 10 to 20 degrees horizontally (and usually 10 degrees vertically), the beam is normally swung in 5 to 10-degree steps, allowing sufficient time in each position for one pulse to travel to maximum range and back. The total power consumption is in the range 250–400 watts, and the acoustic signal at about 50 kc/s, with pulse durations of 0·5 to 2·5 milliseconds, has a power up to perhaps 500 watts. The near-horizontal beam is tilted by about half its beamwidth to reduce troublesome reflections from the sea surface. In one particular equipment another beam is provided at 35 degrees downwards tilt in order to hold contact with fish at closer ranges. Chemical recorders are used for display, although audible indications are also provided sometimes.

(f) More refined fish-finding sonar equipments with narrower beams and adjustable tilt angles. One equipment has a beam with a width of 10 degrees horizontally and only 2 degrees vertically, an acoustic frequency of 61 kc/s, and pulse durations from 1 millisecond upwards. The beam can be swung in both horizontal and vertical planes. It is claimed that a typical performance of the equipment is detection of fish near the bottom in depths up to 200 metres with the beam axis tilted at 20 degrees, i.e. at ranges up to about 500 metres. Exceptionally, detection at ranges of 1,200 metres is claimed.

2 Typical calculation

It is a worthwhile exercise to apply the "sonar equation" discussed in section 2.4 of Chapter 3 to examine the performance of one of these sonar systems. Let us choose the high-power echo-sounder described under (d) above. The basic specification of this equipment is:

Frequency 30 kc/s
Beam 10×15 degrees (on both transmission and reception)
Acoustic power (W) 4 kilowatts
Pulse duration 1 millisecond

Let us assume that the requirement is to detect a single cod-fish
of length 1 metre. This has a target strength (TS) of the order
of −20 dB in dorsal view. (It must be realized how variable
this target strength may be in practice, but the figure given is
probably a fairly typical one.) At 30 kc/s, the absorption loss in
sea-water is typically about 6 dB per kilometre, i.e. $a =$
0·006 dB per metre.

On the assumption that the beam is rectangular in cross-
section (this is actually not strictly true; it is nearer to an
elliptical shape, but the difference is not very significant) it
concentrates the acoustic power in a ratio of about 300: 1
as compared with the radiation from an omni-directional
transducer. Thus the directivity index (DI) is $10 \log_{10} 300$, i.e.
25 dB. From equation (3) of Chapter 3, this gives the transmitted intensity at 1 metre from the transducer as

$$I_S = 36 + 25 - 11 = 50 \text{ dB relative to 1 watt per square metre.}$$

As regards the noise level at the receiver, this we may assume
for present purposes to be dominantly "sea-state" noise
corresponding to sea-state 5. As received by an omni-
directional receiver, this noise would have a level of about
−140 dB relative to 1 watt per square metre per cycle/sec of
bandwidth. For the pulse duration of 1 millisecond, the bandwidth required is 1,000 c/s, so that this raises the noise level by
30 dB. But as the transducer has a narrow beam which "sees"
only one-three-hundredth of the total solid angle from which
noise is assumed to come, this reduces the noise by 25 dB. Thus
the noise intensity is

$$I_N = -140 + 30 - 25 = -135 \text{ dB relative to 1 watt per}$$
$$\text{square metre.}$$

The fish may not pass through the centre of the beam and
the ship may be moving quite fast relative to the fish; thus not
many pulse returns may be received from the target. It is thus
best to assume a recognition differential (D) of 6 dB.

Inserting these various quantities into the sonar equation—
equation (1) of Chapter 3—we obtain

$$2N = 50 + 135 - 20 - 6$$
$$= 159 \text{ dB}$$

From this we want to estimate the range of detection, d, using
equation (2) of Chapter 3. Allowing 10 dB for the anomaly H

(this is almost always a very uncertain guess), this gives

$$20 \log_{10} d + 0 \cdot 006 \, d = 70 \text{ dB approximately.}$$

From this we can work out that d is approximately 1,300 metres, or about 700 fathoms.

In practice a single cod would not often be detected at this range. We have assumed a large fish, the absence of all noise except sea-state noise, quite good propagation conditions, etc. Half this range would be a more realistic figure for regular and reliable detection and this is roughly what the manufacturers claim.

3   Trends for the future

The author's views on the likely developments in sonar for fisheries applications are given in detail in his Buckland Lectures for 1966 which are being published as a companion volume to the present work under the title "Sonar in Fisheries". In general terms, it seems likely that beamwidths will become narrower and narrower (down to even fractions of a degree in some cases) in order that single fish will be detectable at reasonable ranges and very close to the sea-bottom. Since the rate at which an area or volume can be searched with such a narrow beam is very low, it will be necessary to employ rapid electronic methods of beam scanning which will overcome the limitations on mechanical scanning. Such scanning sonar systems have already been developed and should soon be commercially available. Greatly reduced size of equipment is likely as a result of modern electronic developments.

New methods now in the research stage may well enable very narrow beams to be produced from small transducers even at very low frequencies. This would enable very long ranges of detection to be obtained since the losses of acoustic power in the water are small at low frequencies.

The use of sonar systems having a very wide bandwidth of frequency (say 10: 1 ratio of upper to lower frequency in place of the usual very small ratio which is typically 1·03: 1) may enable the fish and other targets to be more positively identified as to size and species.

It will become increasingly necessary to stabilize the position of the acoustic beam in the water irrespective of ship's motion, and this may be achieved by the use of gymbal mounting with stabilizing motion derived from gyros on the ship, or possibly by mounting the transducers on a towed body which will be at a depth great enough to avoid most of the surface motion of the sea.

During the last decade there has been little development in the principles used in commercial sonar for civilian purposes such as fishing. The power and refinement have increased, but the system has remained the same. It is the author's view that this era is nearly at an end, and that great changes will soon be seen.

Appendix I

Description of Trawl

From "The Open Sea, Part II: Fish and Fisheries" by Sir Alister
   Hardy (Collins *New Naturalist*, London, 1959).

There can be no better introduction to the fish and fisheries of the
sea than the sight of a full-sized commercial trawl being emptied of
its catch. Let us watch for a moment as the net is pulled up to the
trawler's side after being dragged along the sea-bed for three hours
or so.

The modern trawl, a gigantic netting bag with an oblong mouth
some 80 feet across, is much more artful than might appear at first
sight. Its upper lip, or head-rope, is raised by a row of floats, while
the heavier lower lip, or foot-rope, sweeps the bottom; and its
opening is spread wide by the corners being pulled sideways by
wooden otter-boards which sheer outwards like kites as they are
towed along. Now the trailing foot-rope, being much longer than
the stretched head-rope above, curves backwards well behind it
and shows us just what a cunning device the trawl is; by the time
the fish on the bottom are disturbed they find themselves actually
covered by a roof of moving net and are, in fact, almost half-way
down the bag already, for the floor of the sea in front acts like an
extension of the mouth. Perhaps its unknown inventor smiled as
broadly as his trawl when he thought of it; if we could ride as
frogmen on top of the net as it moves forward, it might almost
appear as if the fish were carried down its throat on an endless
conveyor belt. The bag tapers behind to a narrow cylinder, the
cod-end, where its catch accumulates.

As the two thick towing warps are wound in, the otter-boards
come into view and are drawn up to the steel gallows, which
project slightly over the side: one towards the bows and another
towards the stern; being heavily bound with iron and bridled with
chains, the boards rattle and clank noisily into place. All at once we
see, abeam of us, a flash of silver as the cod-end breaks the surface;
it floats because so many of the fish are swollen, almost to bursting,
as their air-bladders (buoyancy chambers) are violently distended
by being dragged up so quickly through zones of decreasing pressure.
A little time before this and we would have seen a few gulls circling
the ship: now, drawn as if by magic from miles around, wheeling,
excited, and screaming birds fill the air and repeatedly swoop
down to peck at the fish through the meshes of the net.

The head-rope is drawn up and, after much clutching and
heaving, the deck-hands pull sufficient of the trawl over the side to

allow a rope to be passed around its middle; and now the "cod-end", distended and heavy, is hoisted from the sea. It is swung in-board over a gently rolling deck which has been divided by low wooden partitions into "pounds" to receive the fish; or, if our ship is a very modern one, they would be of gleaming aluminium. For a moment or two the huge bulging mass hangs, dripping and swaying, level with our eyes. What a sight it is! Through the netting, which is stretched to the utmost, stick out fins, spines, tails and gaping mouths, while here and there, large round eyes stare out in un-expected places to give the whole a queer gruesome look. At the bottom of the bag is an opening tied up tightly with a special kind of knot; now an end of this is pulled, and, in a flash, an avalanche of fish cascades on to the deck. The great heap spreads sideways as its slippery components slide and slither in all directions, filling one pound and overflowing into others. Flapping, writhing and gasping, they form a stream of pitiable creatures in distress, but, before long, they will be still, as they pass, with little bouts of quivering, into the fixity of death.

Many of the fish appear glistening white as they lie belly-upwards; but as many, top-side up, show the colours of a host of different kinds. Cod, haddock, whiting and coal-fish show green, grey, buff and black; here and there may be a striped or spotted cat-fish and, if our haul has been far enough to the north, we may get a few scarlet Norway haddocks (*Sebastes*), or "soldiers" as the fishermen call them, or if further to the south perhaps a red gurnard. On the way up the trawl may have caught a herring and a mackerel or two to give a touch of blue or brighter green to the medley, or a male dragonet in courtship dress may flash with rainbow hues. Then there are the flatfish: dark brown plaice flecked with orange spots, speckled turbot and brill, smooth sand-coloured soles, or large skates and rays dappled with a bolder camouflage design; and there are some dogfish, of course. All these are in just one haul, perhaps more than two thousand fish.

Appendix II

The Deep Scattering Layer

From "Subsurface Navigational Hazards", a paper by J. W. Chanslor in the *Journal of the Institute of Navigation*, Vol. 19, 1966, p. 44.

(With small revisions approved by the author.)

(Reproduced by courtesy of U.S. Naval Oceanographic Office.)

Reports frequently indicate the presence of extensive "banks" in areas which are definitely known to be of great depth. These "banks" have two invariable characteristics. First, they are usually reported between 117 and 400 fathoms. Second, they are normally discovered in the daytime. The reason for "phantom bottom" return is that during the day a deep-reflecting or scattering layer often exists in the sea.

World-wide navigational charts indicate shoals rising from the ocean bed and marked ED (existence doubtful). The majority of these are the results of echo-soundings taken by passing ships. As the ship has a schedule to maintain, the captain lacks time to make a complete survey. This, coupled with the possible fear of running aground, results in his sounding report being forwarded to a hydrographic office where it is recorded and quite possibly charted. Depending upon the time of day, it is possible the sounding is from a phantom bottom rather than the true bottom. This deep-scattering layer or phantom bottom exists throughout most of the seas. A ship passing the phantom shoal at a later time will record unlimited depth, but hydrographers are very reluctant to delete possible dangers to navigation from their charts. Once a possible shoal is charted, thousands of other navigators passing in the proximity will give the area a wide berth to avoid the supposed danger. This results in ED's and fictitious banks being charted.

In 1942, a group of physicists were conducting experiments off California with underwater sound-detecting equipment. While working in water thousands of feet deep, a return signal from a depth of about 900 feet was received. This signal was not a sharp echo, as from a submarine on the bottom, but rather a soft reverberation. On sounding sheets or graphs, the return signal resembled a heavy shadow. It did not reflect all the transmitted signal, as the bottom could always be detected, although sometimes only faintly.

Such was the discovery of the deep-scattering layers. Actually, there may be as many as five separate layers. Confusing the situation further was the fact that the deep-scattering layers would rise at

12

sunset and diffuse near the surface. At first light the following day, they would again descend.

It was at first believed that the layers were similar to the iono-sphere layers, i.e. changed due to a physical cause. However, it is now universally accepted that they are due to small marine organisms that rise to the surface at night and descend again at morning. Could this be due to the age-old law of self-preservation? For, as a habitat the open sea offers little refuge. The prey is virtually helpless when sighted by a predator. Some of the sea's organisms assume the same transparency as the water in which they swim to effect concealment. Others lay "smoke screens", have hard shells, etc. Marine organisms of the deep-scattering layers, however, hide in the dark, rising to the surface usually only at night to feed in the plankton-rich waters.

During the hours of daylight sonic-scattering layers range in depths of roughly between 700 and 2,400 feet. They do not always rise to the surface and diffuse at night. Frequently, they may appear as a broad band protruding some 500 feet downward from the surface. The complexity and nature of the layers or bands differ with location and time. Off the coast of California, for example, there are usually three layers—one each at about 950 feet, 1,400 feet, and 1,700 feet.

As yet, not all of the organisms that comprise the scattering layers are known. Among the more numerous occupants, however, are lantern fish and small crustaceans. It was originally thought that the scattering layers consisted of large schools of commercially valuable fish. Such is not the case, however, as the lantern fish, so called because of luminous spots on their sides, range in size of up to about 3 inches. The crustaceans range in size of up to about 1 inch. An idea of their density has also been discovered from the nets towed at night near the surface. Ordinarily from one to five of the smaller organisms (such as the crustaceans) occupy a cubic yard. Exceptionally rich layers may contain up to twenty organisms per cubic yard. The density of fish is, however, probably only of the order of one per 10,000 cubic yards.

With first light, often an hour before sunrise, the first of the scatterers begin to descend, diving at about 25 feet/minute. By sunrise they are about halfway to their nadir, attaining their desired depth about an hour after sunrise. Even here their levels fluctuate somewhat, rising in cloudy or overcast weather and diving even deeper as the sun begins to approach its zenith.

Sonic layers do not exist in the Arctic Ocean, where the polar ice cap cuts off so much sunlight that diatoms cannot exist. Sea life in the south central Pacific Ocean is rather sparse and consequently the deep-scattering layer is quite faint and at times may completely disappear.

Appendix III

Further Discussion of Rectification and Envelopes of Waves

In section 2.2 of Chapter 3 (and in some other less-important places) we have had to use the concept of rectification in regard to the display of the sonar echo signals. It seems desirable to explain this in rather more detail than was reasonable in the main text of Chapter 3.

Basically rectification means the conversion of an alternating quantity into a uni-directional one. There are devices called rectifiers which help to do this in the case of electrical currents; they pass current easily (i.e. with low resistance) when a voltage is applied in one direction, but oppose the flow of current with a high resistance when the voltage is applied in the opposite direction. Thus if such a device is interposed in a circuit carrying an alternating current wave as shown at (a) in Fig. 49, only the positive-going half-cycles of the current can flow, so that the current waveform becomes as shown at (b) in Fig. 49. If this current, which is now all positive, is smoothed by a choke (i.e. an inductance coil or "inductor") or by a condenser (i.e. a capacitance device or "capacitor") as shown in Fig. 50, then the resultant current is a steady "direct-current" or "d.c."

If the current wave is varying in amplitude, as is the case in the sonar echo-signals, then the rectified wave appears as at (c) in Fig. 49. If this is smoothed by a circuit with a response time which is long enough to smooth out the individual half-cycles but short enough to respond to the varying heights of the half-cycles, then the resultant current is a varying d.c. which represents the "envelope" of the wave, i.e. the line joining the peaks of the individual cycles as shown dashed at (c) in Fig. 49. The voltage across the load of the circuit has, of course, the same waveforms as the current.

It should now be clear that when a complex wave, comprising say echo-signal plus noise as in Fig. 41, is rectified and smoothed, the envelope wave which is obtained has an amplitude at any particular instant proportional to the amplitude of the envelope curves which have been drawn in as dashed lines in Fig. 41. The fact that the envelope does *not* have an amplitude equal to that of the echo-signal plus that of the noise can be made clearer by consideration of the phasor diagram in Fig. 51. It will be recalled that phasors were discussed in section 3.3 of Chapter 2, and described as lines in a diagram representing the positions of cranks which drive acoustic sources generating acoustic waves. They can equally well represent electrical current waves. It was explained that when waves are added together, their resultant amplitude is given by the resultant phasor. Thus in Fig. 51, we regard OA as the phasor representing the echo-signal wave, and as the line rotates round O the vertical position of its end A describes the sinusoidal signal wave. We regard the noise as represented by the phasor AB, and as the noise has an amplitude and a phase which are both random, the phasor rotates at a different speed from OA (and at a varying relative speed) and its length varies slowly with time. However, for simplicity we can here merely assume the noise is a constant-amplitude wave of slightly different frequency from the signal, so that AB takes up different positions relative to OA at different times as indicated by AB_1, AB_2, AB_3 and AB_4 in Fig. 51.

Now the envelope amplitude of the resultant wave is clearly given by the length of the phasor OB in its different positions

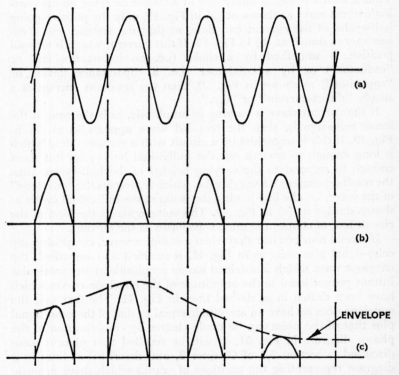

Fig. 49.—Illustrating rectification of current waves: (a) unrectified alternating wave, (b) rectified wave, (c) rectified wave of varying amplitude showing the envelope.

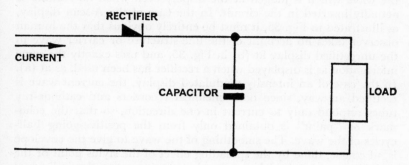

Fig. 50.—Circuit with rectifier and smoothing device.

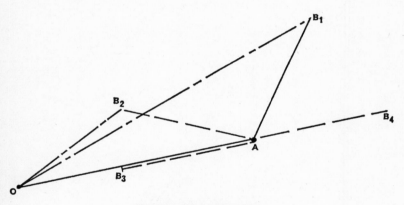

Fig. 51.—Phasor diagram.

OB_1, OB_2, OB_3 and OB_4. At different instants, therefore, the resultant wave can have envelope amplitudes anywhere between the lengths OB_3 and OB_4. If the receiving circuit of the sonar system has a bandwidth only wide enough to pass the echo-pulse without serious distortion (see section 2.1 of Chapter 3), then the noise phasor cannot change its position relative to the signal phasor very quickly, and the conditions represented by OB_1, OB_2, OB_3, OB_4, etc., can persist over most of the duration of any particular echo-pulse. Thus sometimes the echo will be easy to detect (as corresponding to the resultant OB_4) and at other times it will be difficult to detect (as corresponding to OB_3).

It remains perhaps to clarify the idea that it is the envelope of the wave which is judged at the display even when no rectifier is actually inserted in the circuit. In the case of the A-scan display, as illustrated in Fig. 35, it must be entirely obvious that the human observer takes no account of the fine-structure or carrier wave in the unrectified display at (b) in Fig. 35, and uses exactly the same information as is displayed when a rectifier has been used, as at (a). In the case of an intensity-modulated display, the current wave is rectified anyway, since both chemical recorders and cathode-ray tubes respond only to current in one direction, so that the echo-mark or "paint" is obtained only from the positive-going half-cycles of the wave. The smoothing of the wave to give the envelope is, of course, done by the spreading effect of the stylus point or the cathode-ray spot, which are too large to separate the individual cycles of the wave.

Appendix IV

Further Reading

(A few suggestions, necessarily selected rather arbitrarily from a vast bibliography.)

CHAPTER 1

Section 1   Sir John Edgell: "Sea Surveys: Britain's Contribution to Hydrography", H.M. Stationery Office, London, 1965.
                 Annual reports of the various laboratories and Councils, e.g. "Annual Report of the National Oceanographic Council, 1963-64", Cambridge University Press, 1965. (Deals with National Institute of Oceanography.)

Section 2.1   Sir Alister Hardy: "The Open Sea, Part II: Fish and Fisheries", Collins *New Naturalist*, London, 1959.
                 R. E. Craig: "The Fisheries Applications of Sonar", *J. Brit. Inst. Radio Engrs.*, **25,** 1963, p. 201.
                 R. Balls: "Fish Capture", Edward Arnold, London, 1961.
                 A collection of up-to-date papers covering the whole field is in "Modern Fishing Gear of the World", Fishing News (Books), London, 1964.

Section 2.2   F. R. Harden Jones: "Further observations on the movements of herring (*Clupea harengus L.*) shoals in relation to the tidal current", *J. du Conseil international pour l'Exploration de la Mer*, **27,** 1962, p. 52.
                 A. R. Margetts: "The Fishing of Trawls and Seines", *World Fishing*, December, 1963, p. 63, and January, 1964, p. 48.
                 H. Mohr: "Reaction of Herring to Fishing Gear Revealed by Echo-Sounding", in *Modern Fishing Gear of the World*, Fishing News (Books), London, 1964, p. 253.

Section 2.3   G. E. R. Deacon (editor): "Oceans", Paul Hamlyn, London, 1962 (includes a full list of books on oceans and oceanography).

Section 2.4   E. G. R. Taylor: "The Haven-Finding Art: A History of Navigation from Odysseus to Captain Cook", Hollis and Carter, London, 1956.
                 G. J. Sonnenberg: "Radar and Electronic Navigation", Newnes, London, 1955.
                 "The Use of Radar at Sea", Hollis and Carter, London, 1965.

E. Ahrens: "Automatic Echo-sounding Systems", *J. Inst. Navigation*, **13**, 1960, p. 173.

J. W. Chanslor: "Subsurface Navigational Hazards", *ibid*, **19**, 1966, p. 41.

Section 2.5   A. H. Stride: "Geological Interpretation of Asdic Recorders", *Internat. Hydrographic Rev.*, **38**, 1961, p. 131.

Section 2.7   B. K. Gazey and J. C. Morris: "An underwater acoustic telephone for free-swimming divers", *Electronic Engg.*, **36**, 1964, p. 364.

Section 3.1   K. O. Emery, A. S. Merrill and J. V. A. Trumbull: "Geology and biology of the sea-floor as deduced from simultaneous photographs and samples", *Limnology and Oceanography*, **10**, 1965, p. 1.

R. I. Currie: "The Indian Ocean Standard Net", *Deep-Sea Res.*, **10**, 1963, p. 27.

Section 3.2   J. Piccard and R. S. Dietz: "Oceanographic observations by the bathyscaph 'Trieste' (1953-1956)", *Deep-Sea Res.*, **4**, 1957, p. 221.

G. L. Clarke and G. K. Wertheim: "Measurements of illumination at great depths and at night in the Atlantic Ocean by means of a new bathyphotometer", *Deep-Sea Res.*, **3**, 1956, p. 189.

R. E. Craig and R. L. Craig: "The Prediction of undersea light, with special reference to Scottish fishing areas", *Photochemistry and Photobiology*, **4**, 1965, p. 633.

Section 3.3   A. S. Laughton: "A new deep-sea underwater camera", *Deep-Sea Res.*, **4**, 1957, p. 120.

R. Livingstone: "Underwater television observations of Haddock (*Melanogrammus aeglefinus* [*Linnaeus*]) in the cod-end", *J. du Conseil international pour l'Exploration de la Mer*, **27**, 1962, p. 43.

R. E. Craig and R. Priestley: "Undersea photography in marine research", *Marine Research*, 1963, No. 1, H.M.S.O.

E. R. Cross: "Underwater Photography and Television", Exposition Press, New York, 1954.

H. Barnes: "Underwater Television", in "Oceanography and Marine Biology, Vol. 1", George Allen & Unwin, London, 1963.

V. G. Welsby, J. H. S. Blaxter and C. J. Chapman: "Electronically scanned sonar in the investigation of fish behaviour", *Nature*, **199**, 1963, p. 980.

Section 3.5   J. N. Carruthers: "A simple current-measuring bottle for fishermen", *Fishing News*, 12 May, 1961, p. 8.

M. J. Tucker: "The N.I.O. depth telemeter", *Proc. Int. Telemetering Conference* (Institution of Electrical Engineers), **1**, 1963, p. 224.

Section 3.6   L. Kay: "Orientation of bats and men by ultrasonic echo location", *Brit. Communications and Electronics*, **8**, 1961, p. 582.

M. P. Fish, A. S. Kelsey and W. H. Mowbray: "Studies on the production of underwater sound by North Atlantic coastal fishes", *J. Marine Research*, **11**, 1952, p. 180.

G. Freytag: "Bio-acoustical detection of fish: possibilities and future aspects", *Modern Fishing Gear of the World*, No. 2, 1963, p. 400.

T. Hashimoto and Y. Maniwa: "Frequency analysis of marine sounds", *ibid*, p. 440.

J. M. Moulton: "Underwater sound: Biological aspects", in "Oceanography and Marine Biology, Vol. 2", George Allen & Unwin, London, 1964.

W. N. Tavolga (editor): "Marine Bio-Acoustics", Pergamon (Oxford), 1964.

F. P. Shepard: "The Earth beneath the Sea", Oxford University Press, 1959.

CHAPTERS 2, 3, and 4

Some more advanced books are:

A. B. Wood: "A Textbook of Sound", Bell (London), 1949.

L. E. Kinsler and A. R. Frey: "Fundamentals of Acoustics", Wiley (New York), 1962.

P. M. Morse: "Vibration and Sound", McGraw-Hill (New York), 1948.

V. M. Albers: "Underwater Acoustics Handbook", Pennsylvania State University Press, 1961.

J. W. Horton: "Fundamentals of Sonar", U.S. Naval Inst., Annapolis, 1957.

D. G. Tucker and B. K. Gazey: "Applied Underwater Acoustics", Pergamon (Oxford), 1966.

F. V. Hunt: "Electroacoustics: The Analysis of Transduction and its Historical Background", Harvard University Press, 1954.

L. Guieysse and P. Sabathé: "Acoustique Sous-Marine" (in French), Dunod, Paris, 1964.

Index

Absorption losses, 65
Acoustic impedance, 64
Acoustic pressure, 58
Acoustic waves, 51
Array, 71
A-scan, 95
Aural detection (of sonar signals), 94

Baffle, 77
Band-limited noise, 105
Bandwidth, 101
Bathyscaphe, 29
Beams, 66, 76
Beamwidth, 77
Bottom reverberation, 114

Cameras, underwater, 31, 39
Canals, 46
Cathode-ray displays, 95
Chemical recorder, 94
Cores (of sea-bed), 28, 37
Corer, 28, 36
Cosine relation, 60
Critical angle, 80

Decibel, 64
Deep scattering layer (d.s.l.), 24
Demersal fishing, 20
Depth of trawl, 49
Directional pattern (or response), 73
Directivity factor (and index), 120
Displacement, 58
Displays, 93
Diving, 26
Doppler shift, 108
Drift net, 20

Echoes, 87
Echo-location, 54
Echo-sounders, 91
Electrostrictive transducer, 98
Envelopes of waves, 133

Far-field, 66
Fish behaviour (with respect to net), 23
Fish catching, 18
Fisheries research, 22

Geology, marine, 26

Harbours, etc., 26
Hard boundary, 85
Herring, 20

Illumination, underwater, 30
Impedance (acoustic), 64
Intensity (acoustic), 62
Intensity-modulation, 95
Interference of waves, 67
Inverse-square law, 63
Isotropic noise, 120

Jelly bottle, 49

Lead, sounding, 27
Light, loss in water, 30
Losses (acoustic) in sea-water, 65

Magnetostrictive transducer, 97
Midwater trawls, 21
Minor lobes, 76

Naval operations, 27
Navigation, 25
Noise, 104

Oceanography, 24

Particle velocity, 58
Passive acoustic methods, 54
Pelagic fishing, 20
Phase angles, 69
Phase difference, 69
Phase shift, 70
Phasor, 70

Piezo-electric transducer, 98
Ping, 55
Plane wave, 62
Polar patterns, 73
Pressure release boundary, 85
Pulse duration, 100
Purse seine net, 20

Q-factor, 103

Radian, 58
Radio waves in water, 32
Recognition differential, 119, 121
Rectification, 107, 133
Reflection, 78
Refraction, 78, 86
Resistance (acoustic), 64, 85
Resolution (of picture), 53
Resolution of targets, 104
Resonance, 103
Reverberation, 111
Reversing bottles, 28
Rho-cee rubber, 99
Ring net, 20
Rivers, 47
R.m.s. (root-mean-square), 64, 105

Salinity, 29
Sampling, 27
Sandwich transducers, 99
Scattering cross-section, 90
Sea-bed lock, 124
Sea-bottom (or sea-floor), 19, 26, 28, 37, 41, 44, 45, 48
Sea-mount, 45
Sea-state noise, 104
Seismic shooting, 56
Shear waves, 80
Signal-to-noise ratio (SNR), 107

Signal-to-reverberation ratio (SRR), 112
Simple harmonic motion, 58
(Sin x)/x pattern, 76
Sinusoid, 58
Snell's Law, 80
Soft boundary, 85
Sonar, 23, 55
Sonar equation, 119, 125
Sounding lead, 27
Spectrum (of pulse), 101
Spherical wave, 62
Spreading loss, 64
Spreading wave, 62
Surface reverberation, 116

Target, 87
Target strength, 89
—— of fish, 126
Telemetry, 49
Television, underwater, 31, 43
Temperature, 28, 37
Thermal noise, 104
Threshold of detection, 107
Time-base, 93
Total internal reflection, 80
Training of beams, 125
Transducer, 77, 97
Transmission anomaly, 120
Trawl, 20, 22, 29, 50, 129

Velocity gradient, 87
Velocity of propagation, 66
Vision, underwater, 30
Volume reverberation, 114

Wave front, 86
Wavelength, 60
White-line recording, 124